PARALLEL LIVES

MARYAM DIENER

Quadrant
Books

First published in 2024 by Quadrant Books
Suite 2, Top Floor, 7 Dyer Street, Cirencester,
Gloucestershire, GL7 2PF.

A catalogue record for this book is available
from the British Library.

p. 1: Photo by Edith Tudor-Hart. Copyright the
Estate of W. Suschitzky. Courtesy of Fotohof.

Parallel Lives
Paperback ISBN 978-1-7384598-4-1

Designed by Zak Group
Printed in Italy

for CF

At the base of the Lawn Road Flats, Edith raises her
Rolleiflex camera to her hip to photograph the children
playing hide and seek on the stairs. Guests stand on
pale pink balconies in blazing sunshine, summer hats
peeking out from behind the concrete. The children bob
out over the edges then retreat. *Click*. Edith smiles. The
building, the Isokon, is eerily beautiful, an alien space-
ship suspended in the leafy backstreets of Hampstead.

She photographs the architect, the owners and the
guests. This is so much more than just a building. All
the attendees, fashionably attired – the women in tight-
waisted pattern dresses, their hair bobbed, the men dap-
per in light suits – would agree that this place is more
than an aesthetic statement. It is a new way of living. The
promise of a community of likeminded individuals, all
focusing on their work and their passions, on collabora-
tion. In these thirty-four 'minimum' flats, furniture will
be built in or provided, so all the occupants need bring
are their books and a vase of flowers. Everything from
shoe-cleaning to laundry will be done for them, their
meals supplied from a communal kitchen. These future
occupants, Bauhaus émigrés, artists, writers, designers
and socialist sympathisers, will be free to concentrate
entirely on the things they love.

Edith photographs the married couple behind this philosophy, Jack and Molly Pritchard. It is Molly who crafted
the brief for the Lawn Road Flats, inspired by Walter
Gropius's notion of 'minimum dwelling', announced to the
world just five years earlier at the famous 1929 C.I.A.M. conference on the social and economic potential of architecture. But it is not her husband's shoulder that Molly's hand
lingers on so tenderly. Instead, her arm is draped around
the building's architect in a way that suggests much more
than a working relationship. The architect's name is Wells
Coates, an elegant man in an open white shirt with a tidy,

slim moustache. It was through the encouragement of her husband Jack that Molly started this relationship. Jack is also involved in an extramarital affair, with Edith's sister-in-law, Beatrix. The four of them originally planned to build houses on this plot of land and live adjacently.

Born in Tokyo, Coates takes inspiration from the Japanese aesthetic concepts of simplicity and sobriety. He recently finished designing the radio studios at the BBC, with their innovative curved desk from which the announcer can move swiftly from spot to spot and mix sounds from ten different rooms. For this he invented an ingenious ceiling-mounted microphone that can be swung to reach all parts of the studio, and a rotating operating table with seven different surfaces for the creation of sound effects. But more than his groundbreaking designs, it is his personal magnetism that holds Jack and Molly's fascination.

Edith photographs Alexander, her own husband, captured smiling as he herds some of the children up the stairs to get snacks.

She photographs Alexander's sister, Beatrix, looking out from under a vast wide-brimmed hat.

She photographs the celebrated statistician and intellectual Robert Kuczynski and his wife, Berta, as they talk to one of their daughters.

She photographs the building from all different angles. It has come alive with the people flowing in and out of its organic structure.

The crowd walk up the stairs, and a man with a long face and intelligent forehead turns and looks directly at her. With its viewfinder mounted on top, Edith's Rolleiflex must be held at the waist, leaving her vulnerable, her face entirely exposed to this man's gaze.

As he looks at her, a malaise floods her body from head to toe, while her palms instantly begin to sweat. In that moment, her emotions seem almost tangible, like particles floating out into the hot air. She stays there motionless for a minute. Time is frozen.

She knew he would be here. It is her job to know these things, and she has something important to say to him. Yet the sight of him still floors her.

Edith had met Arnold when she was just eighteen, at her father's bookshop in Vienna where she worked after school. She was busy rearranging the shelves and making space for new titles when she felt the gaze, over her shoulder, of a man standing in the aisle.

The shop was in one of the city's most overcrowded and disadvantaged neighbourhoods, the Favoriten District, where Edith had grown up. It had been Vienna's first social-democratic bookshop, and the first of any kind in this working-class area, after a long fight with the government for permission. Edith's father thought it an important tool in educating the masses, in opening the eyes of the disadvantaged to their oppression, and he published and sold books there at prices affordable for the people. Their subjects spanned pacifism, psychoanalysis, psychiatry, women's rights, family planning, alcoholism and sexual health, and the shop became a publishing house with a reputation among intellectuals for producing and selling titles that could not be found elsewhere.

That day, Edith turned around and met the man's gaze. He was much older than her, but when he smiled, as he did at that exact moment, his expression was disarming and infectious. He had wide shoulders, and his curly blond hair and clear blue eyes gave him a winningly youthful charm.

Edith's light brown hair was boyishly cropped above the perfectly arched eyebrows that framed her big grey eyes – eyes that showed a composure belying her years.

In perfect German, but with a trace of an accent, he asked for a copy of *Impulsive Character* by Wilhelm Reich. Reich was a Freud disciple, and his writing was sold under the counter because it was classified as pornographic. Reich believed that good sex equated to good mental health, and problems such as anxiety or depression were the result of people repressing their sexual urges.

'And what are you looking for in the writing of Reich?' she said provocatively.

Surprised to find a young girl familiar with Reich's work, he smiled gently. She was, he realised, not just beautiful; there was strength and wit in those eyes. A chemistry graduate, he was also an expert in the theories of Reich and involved in setting up sexual health clinics in the area to promote progressive ideas on sexual freedom and birth control.

'Maybe you would like to join me at Reich's lecture at the Urania Observatory next week?' he asked quietly.

She didn't reply but knew that she would go.

Edith blinks away the memory. She is back again, in the heart of the Lawn Road opening, where she must document this historic moment.

The guests are converging now, waiting for the speech.

Click. Near Molly and Wells, Edith's sister-in-law Beatrix stands out from the crowd in her wide-brimmed hat. Beatrix's hand brushes against Jack's arm, and he tucks a loose strand of her hair behind her ears. Their daughter is running around the building somewhere, after her half-brothers. These are not traditional people. They advocate for reform of living at every level: architectural, domestic, social, sexual.

Click. Edith can't help it. She photographs Arnold again, standing on the balcony below her. He gave Edith the camera she is now using to photograph him. Is Josephine here?

After the Reich lecture, eight years before, Arnold suggested they get a drink together. They soon sat at a café around the corner on the Stubenring, where Arnold began to tell Edith his story.

Arnold was originally Slovak, from a Jewish Orthodox family that emigrated to Vienna when he was a child. Smiling wryly, he admitted that, to his family's despair, he had refused to adopt the strict rules of the religion in favour of his more political interests. He soon became engaged with the Communist Youth. He was a radical thinker, and saw the urgent need for a programme of working-class education. This interested Edith very much.

Edith's father had also renounced his faith to become an atheist and a socialist. Questions of social and economic reform dominated the discourse of Edith's childhood and adolescence. She was six when the First World War broke out, and afterwards the tenth district was left in a state of privation disproportionate to the rest of the city. Many of the schools closed, and children became weak from hunger and, often, tuberculosis. After peace was restored, Edith was sent to Sweden for a few months to regain her strength, but most were not so lucky. Inequality and unrest abounded.

Upon her return to Austria, it became clear that the war's fallout was far from over. She saw malnourished children on the streets, beggars, queues of unemployed young workers. Her heart wrenched, unable to stand by as misery compounded itself all around, she threw herself into fighting social injustice. Visiting a school in the Favoriten district, she was shocked to see how poor the education was, how little children got to eat and how the war had laid waste to the entire education system it had relied upon, many institutions commandeered by the military.

Wandering the shabby halls, there seemed to her a distinct absence of staff, and those she saw looked harried and drawn, barely taking the time to notice her. She entered a classroom with her guide and seated herself next to a group of unattended young children dressed in coats and hats to fend off the cold. They were perhaps seven or eight years old and showing clear signs of malnourishment. But as she played games with them and they grew in confidence, their faces seeming to shed the signs of hunger and abandonment, and she felt a warmth growing inside her as laughter echoed off the peeling walls.

She felt the urgency to act growing ever stronger and resolved to do what she could to fix the education system, and to do so with progressive values at the forefront. She convinced some Jewish mothers to help, and together they started to give free lessons to children denied them elsewhere. Their inspiration was Lili Roubiczek, a progressive Czech educator who believed in communal living, with teachers boarding at school on weekdays. While they didn't go that far, Edith and the mothers took seriously her ideas on training teachers in language, sociology and psychology, so that they could provide a more humanistic and well-rounded education.

Throughout this postwar period, the Russian Revolution bubbled away in the background, with news of mutinies, protests and violence. Leninist revolutionary politics surrounded Edith as she grew up, and by sixteen she was volunteering in a local Montessori-inspired nursery school, where her worldview was galvanised by the hotbed of political activity she found there and the wealth of socialist contacts she made.

Arnold and Edith continued to recount their stories as dusk fell and a warm nocturnal glow suffused the café. And through the smoke that coiled around them as she lit cigarettes one after another, the alluringly enigmatic and self-assured man in front of her gradually came into focus.

A trader's son, he had been expected to follow his father into the business, but instead studied for a physics degree where he was drawn to Trotsky and his internationalism. His parents were angry at his choice of profession, let alone his politics, but Arnold believed it better to make your own way in life, that nothing should stand in the way of your passions. Edith agreed. They smiled at each other. And as they shared their political views over the tinkle of late-night drinks, he found he had an urgent desire to touch her hand.

Arnold told her straight away that he lived with his wife, Josephine, who, like Edith, was training to be a

Montessori teacher. Edith wondered where Josephine was at that moment, while Arnold sat in the café with her, his chair sliding closer as he whispered in her ear.

Arnold and Edith could not stay away from one other.

In the weeks after the Reich lecture, they met regularly in cafés and parks during the day, and at night swam naked in the Stürzelwasser and the Danube, their bodies luminous against the pitch-dark. He lived with Josephine, and Edith with her parents, but one day Arnold turned up to meet her with the keys to an empty apartment that his friend was lending him. She tried to hide her insecurity about this new development and pulled herself together. 'Yes,' she nodded. 'Let's go.'

Edith's upbringing had been far from conservative or bourgeois. As well as propagating politically progressive ideas, her father's bookshop had several times found itself in serious trouble for promoting women's emancipation and sexual freedom. So Edith did know about sex and contraception. And yet nobody really knows, do they, before it happens? There are things that a pamphlet in a bookshop can't tell a young girl.

Afterwards she lay in a square of sunshine thrown down from a window, surrounded by unfamiliar belongings in this strange apartment, and knew she was very much in love with the mysterious man beside her.

From the moment Arnold first put the camera in her hands, Edith saw photography as a way of documenting the social injustice she found around her every day in Vienna. He had shown her how her politics and keen eye for observation could complement one another. Scenes of the indigent and forgotten filled her lens as she walked through the city in search of her next subject. She took pictures of veterans unfit to work, of the unemployed assembling on the streets, of fathers carrying their children and begging by the side of the road. She went to slums and took pictures of the women living there in bleak conditions.

She did not want to just record events, but to influence and provoke awareness with her camera. Through these heartbreaking images, she could express her stark social criticism of a system that was not supporting those in most need. Though she was sometimes paid when magazines published her work, the camera was so much more than a way to make a living. If used with feeling and imagination, it was an integral way of recording and influencing the world, for promoting human understanding and sensitivity. Photography and its development provided a direct line to the masses, and had quickly became a vehicle for the Left to mobilise and bring new people into the fold. Edith would take advantage of that as much as she could.

Through her photography she felt connected with Arnold even when they could not be together. He was not only married, but also an agent for the Comintern – The Communist International, a Soviet-controlled organisation promoting world revolution. Edith became accustomed to not seeing him for long periods of time. Her Montessori teacher-training also took her to England, where she was introduced to other Communist sympathisers including child psychologist Beatrix Tudor-Hart and her brother, Dr Alexander Tudor-Hart. Edith continued an intense correspondence with these siblings for nearly a decade after they met, seeing them whenever she could in Vienna or England.

Edith's love of photography led her to the Bauhaus in Dessau, where she studied while working as a kindergarten teacher. When Edith arrived there in 1928, she registered not in the department of photography, but at the school's famous foundation course. In the end, though, it was not her illustrious professors but another personality who had a profound influence on her, the architect Hannes Meyer, under whose directorship the school was in the midst of a radical transformation. Mayer was shifting the school's philosophy towards the communal and practical in a revolutionary move to the left. 'The new way to build,' he called it, and from then on the institution's priority would be designs that could fulfil social needs with minimal cost and maximum efficiency.

Edith was so awed by the work that she published an article about the school's revolutionary new direction in an English art journal. She had found herself in a crucible of transformative thinking, and it wasn't long before fellow Communist radicals made themselves known to her. With them her political education continued alongside her artistic development. But her time at the Bauhaus was cut short. A true adept of Hannes Meyer, when she heard of his resignation, she decided to leave as well.

Outside the school and a teacher still, she continued to document the ordinary life of Vienna's inhabitants, without embellishing or hiding from the facts. Committed to capturing unadulterated truths, she photographed the left behind, the war wounded, gypsies, the blind or deaf, shining a light on what society would rather ignore. She won a photography prize at a socialist-leaning magazine called *Der Kuckuck*, after which she got a job at the local office of *Tass*, the leading Soviet news agency. Arnold was her support, her sounding board, her world, but she knew that he did not belong to her.

One day he appeared at her desk at *Tass* and asked to speak privately. She made excuses to her colleagues and walked with him to Cafe Minesterium, where they'd had their first drink together. As they walked, she instinctively knew that this would be the end of their relationship, at least for now.

When they sat down, Arnold told her that some of his colleagues engaged in underground activities had been arrested over the last few days. Josephine was already in Moscow, and he was going to leave immediately to join her.

Edith remained surprisingly composed, her jaw set and her eyes glazed and distracted with an air of affected boredom. Affected but effective, and so much so that Arnold was struck by the idea that she must have another lover.

'I do,' she replied and turned away from him.

He gave her a small card with his address.

'My name will be Otto,' he said, 'when you find me again.'

Now, through the crowd outside the Lawn Road Flats, she watches him. 'Only the liberation of the natural capacity for love in human beings can master their sadistic destructiveness,' Reich said. Love should not be contained. It will conquer.

Miss Thelma Cazalet, a Feminist and Conservative Party MP, smashes a bottle of beer on to the side of the flats and declares them open. As beer drips down the concrete and the crowd cheers, Edith photographs her closest friend from Vienna, Litzi Friedmann. They wave at each other.

Black-haired and with the darkest eyes, Litzi has a mercurial face that Edith loves. She can be arrestingly beautiful or entirely invisible depending on her mood. She and her new husband Kim are sharing a joke, silhouetted against the pale pink concrete of the wall behind. Kim is also a shifting creature, hard if not impossible to capture in a photograph. With his upper-class English voice and expensive clothes, he is oddly attractive when he wants to be, yet can slip through a crowd unnoticed. Edith thinks that Kim could be of great use to the cause – if she could just get him to meet Arnold. Not here though, at this conspicuous party.

Knepler, a famous Austrian pianist and musicologist, introduced Edith to Litzi at a Communist meeting in a smoke-filled Viennese apartment. He knew they would have common ground – Litzi's parents were also left-wing activists, and she was highly engaged in the political scene. Litzi had been married by age eighteen but divorced just fourteen months later, before becoming a committed member of the Communist Party. Similarly, in the years after Arnold left Vienna, Edith became an experienced activist and courier for the Communist Party of Austria (KPO). Edith was excited to meet a woman fighter ready to take risks for her beliefs. They had been friends and comrades ever since, and now

Edith walks over to speak with her, never losing sight of where Arnold is positioned in the crowd.

This building, Edith thinks, is unusual in a way that could prove extremely useful. It is long and thin but built at an angle so not easily observed from the road. A quiet woodland area behind it could be used to reach Belsize Park Tube station. Most importantly, there are two staircases, one external, one internal. It would be easy to see if you'd been followed into the building. And once inside, the follower would find it hard to tell which floor or flat you had entered. Or indeed, whether you had slipped into the woods and away on the Tube.

Arnold was Edith's first and greatest love. But Edith has always been pragmatic. After Arnold left Vienna, Edith's relationship with Alexander Tudor-Hart, her future husband, intensified. She attended a Communist rally with him in England and was immediately deported for her involvement. He felt responsible for her expulsion and kept writing to her and visiting her in Vienna. Although Alexander was married with a daughter, their political friendship was unmistakably building into something more.

Meanwhile, social and political tensions were on the rise, soon to reach boiling point. The Great Depression came and with it mass unemployment and an inflation that ate people's savings to the bone. Then when Hitler became Chancellor of Germany, in 1933, Nazi sympathisers, who wanted Germany and Austria reunited, threatened the Austrian state from within.

With the Right on the rise, Austrian Chancellor Engelbert Dollfuss clamped down on Communists. Dollfuss introduced press censorship and banned all political demonstrations, including strikes. After the May Day demonstrations of 1933, eight hundred Communists were rounded up. Vienna was becoming heated, lawless and increasingly anti-democratic. Inspired by the example of Fascist Italy, the Austrian Parliament was soon abolished and the constitution discarded.

So the stakes were high when Edith was walking down the Liechtensteinstrasse with letters from the Party under her arm. She hesitated outside the bookshop that served as a drop-off point. Two policemen were crossing the road in her direction with intent, and something told her it was no book they were looking for. Her heart began to pound, but she continued into the shop, not wanting to draw attention to herself by walking away.

The policemen followed her inside. She began to casually browse the shelves. She wouldn't be able to deny that she was carrying documents for the Party, but she bided her time – removing various titles from shelves, reading blurbs, pretending to decide which texts to buy until they made their move. She didn't have long to wait.

At the station, Edith answered every question carefully. She said she was a trained kindergarten teacher but that she hadn't been working for the last three years and instead made money as a press photographer. Yes, her father was co-owner of a bookshop in Favoritenstrasse. No, she was not a member of any political organisation. Yes, she did happen to be carrying Lenin's biography in her bag, but it was just out of curiosity, Sir. Just curiosity.

The letters, however, could not be easily explained away. She tried to act dumb, telling her interrogators that a stranger in a café had asked her to deliver some documents for him, claiming he worked for a humanitarian organisation. She had not asked about the contents. She suggested that she was gullible, not revolutionary, an intellectual, horn-rimmed glasses and all, dutifully doing an acquaintance a favour and stopping en route to browse her favourite bookshop.

There were four envelopes. The most damning to Edith was a circular calling for protest – for demonstrations in front of prisons and a 'united front' in support of political prisoners. In the wake of Dollfuss's fascistic power grab, the circular demanded the formation of opposition groups among Social Democratic workers. It suggested protests against the banning of the KPO and aimed to inspire sympathisers to disseminate more party propaganda.

It only took one visit to Edith's parents' house for the police to see that this circular had been mimeographed there.

Back in the interrogation room, Edith stared at the wall in silence while they made notes about her appearance, what she was wearing, her mannerisms: her sky blue jumper and navy blue skirt. Her grey tights and black shoes. Her upright posture. Her blue-grey eyes …

Then they put her in detention, which was filling up with collaborators and Communists under Dollfuss's orders.

One day during the month that Edith was in prison, Litzi opened the door of her parents' house to see a dashing Englishman standing at the door. He put out his hand to introduce himself and flashed her an inquisitive smile.

'My name is Kim Philby, and I am here to learn German,' he said. 'We have mutual friends in Paris who thought your family might be looking for a lodger.'

'How much money do you have?' she asked, and he smiled at her directness. He was slim and pale, wearing an expensive-looking suit. His manners, too, spoke of a costly education. He answered that he had received £100 for his twenty-first birthday, which he was hoping would last a year in Vienna. This sum, she replied, would last a year with £25 left over for him to give to the International Organisation for Aid to Revolutionaries.

As Kim walked into the house, he stole a long look at Litzi's unusually dark hair and bare legs. He thought that he would enjoy his time in Austria very much.

Edith had been communicating with Alexander Tudor-Hart for years now, exchanging letters and photographs. Not long after she had been imprisoned, she received an envelope from him. She remembered with a sad smile that she had promised Alexander photos *'ohne kleider'*, that is to say naked, the morning of her arrest. This clearly had not happened.

She opened it and started to read: he was divorcing his wife.

She placed the letter thoughtfully back in the envelope. Alexander loved her, Edith was sure of it.

Outside of her prison-cell walls, tensions were escalating quickly. The Right-wing government was constantly clashing with socialist forces and hundreds were dying in armed street conflicts. Closer to home, her family's bookshop was under threat. Her father was suffering from a terrible depression and crying for hours every day, desperate to get Edith out of prison and out of harm's way. He had even tried to take his life.

Sitting on the cold concrete floor, her gaze following the cracks in the wall like spiderwebs, Edith hatched a plan.

Her father's brilliant lawyers ensured that Edith was soon released from jail while she awaited her trial. She swore to the authorities that she would remain in Vienna during the penal procedure, but instead she planned her marriage to the recently divorced Alexander.

Alexander's sister, Beatrix, was delighted with the idea. She wrote to Edith and hinted that his current wife – a doctor herself, and bisexual – was by no means devastated by the divorce. Beatrix also wrote to Edith about her own life. She now had a child with her lover, Jack Pritchard, and she described the architectural project they were involved in together in Hampstead. Beatrix insisted that she would ask Jack to commission Edith as the on-site photographer for the construction and opening of what would be an iconic landmark and revolutionary social experiment.

Edith married Alexander at the British Consulate and fled to England. Alexander's ex-wife provided Edith with the health certificate she needed to remain in the UK, without her having to go through formalities as a Jewish immigrant. Suddenly, after years of turmoil, she felt safe.

She moved into Alexander's house at 68 Acre Lane in Brixton, where they lived with other Communists. She also rented a studio on Haverstock Hill, minutes from the Lawn Road Flats. Though the tiny studio was always filled with the acrid, metallic smell of chemical developer, she had a bed there for when she didn't want to travel back to Brixton after producing photographs, or for when she needed privacy for her more clandestine endeavours. She continued her work for the Party, and on top of that the NKVD secret service, making deliveries and passing on information.

While Edith was safely in London hunched over photos in her dark room, things were not so tranquil back in Vienna. One early evening, Kim and Litzi had been at home together when all the lights cut out. The telephone rang and a male voice spoke urgently, telling them to meet him in a café. The simmering hostility in the city had finally boiled over into all-out violence. The streets felt eerie: there were strikes, power cuts, arrests and executions. Litzi and Kim rushed to the café through patrols and roadblocks, using Kim's British passport as cover, and they sat in the appointed café for two hours before anyone turned up. When their contact arrived, the conversation was short. The Communist Party wanted to know if they were willing to install a machinegun post in the city.

Recently graduated from Cambridge university, Kim had very little first-hand experience of either women or revolution when he had first met Litzi. She gave him a crash course in both and soon they were working and sleeping together. They raised funds, performed courier tasks and helped activists flee Vienna.

The two of them made a glamorous couple. He might have come across every bit the English gentleman, but beneath his cultured, clean-cut, cut-glass stylings was a man who enjoyed living on the edge, an athlete who felt equally at home in the boxing ring as the debating club.

Born in the Punjab, he had been taken back to England by his mother after his parents separated. But since his father had converted to Islam and become the advisor of Ibn Saud, the first king of Saudi Arabia, he had visited him and spent time in the desert with the Bedouins, discovering a way of life far more exhilarating and authentic than that of his friends summering on the Riviera. This he told Litzi one night while preparing schnapps. Elegant and sharply dressed as always, Kim had an intensity not seen till now, and she was taken by his mystique. In turn, Litzi's exotic beauty, her confidence and strength of personality had certainly worked their magic on this young man, not yet well acquainted with the opposite sex.

Now very much a partnership, they agreed to the machine gun proposal and spent the next afternoon in the café waiting for further instructions only for no one to appear. The day after they returned to the café, but the contact never did. And so the lovers changed tack and helped their cause by providing food and clothes to strikers and finding hiding places for hunted revolutionaries. Around them, thousands of people were being arrested, with anyone suspected of having a leadership role executed. With Litzi's history of arrests and activism it would be only a matter of time before they arrested her, and there would be no escape with an Austrian passport in her purse.

Instead, Kim married Litzi in the Vienna Town Hall and gave her British citizenship. Like Edith the year before, Litzi found herself heading to London. As soon as the newlyweds were installed at Kim's parents' house in West Hampstead, Litzi contacted Edith and they began to meet almost every day, discussing their lives and loves. Kim would sometimes come too, lounging on Edith's bed in the photographic studio, studying her work. Kim was keen to take his own activities to the next level. He wanted an introduction into Edith's world.

'It's been a long time,' Edith says to Arnold with a smile, the party all but forgotten. 'There is someone I think you should meet.'

'Let's arrange something, but I'm afraid I must go now.'

'Of course,' Edith nods, torn. She would like to reach out and take his hand, lay it against her cheek, but she does not. Instead, she is the first to turn away.

Uncharacteristically shaken by this encounter, she walks straight into a woman of a similar age. This woman has a large nose and an even larger smile, framed by black hair cut short above the neck and an angled hat. There is an immediate, disarming wildness about that smile.

'Apologies,' Edith says.

'Not at all,' replies the woman, with a twinkle in her dark eyes. She walks over to Robert Kuczynski and his wife Bertha, who even at first glance could only be her parents, so much does she reflect their looks and mannerisms. This is Ursula.

URSULA KUCZYNSKI

Due to the parallel but never intersecting nature of their work, Edith would never know how much she had in common with Ursula. Edith worked for the NKVD. Ursula and her family worked for the GRU, the Russian military intelligence agency. Similar goals but without cross-pollination.

The Kuczynskis were a wealthy, well-connected German–Jewish family, all rebellious anti-Fascists. They had arrived in the UK in the first wave of refugees after Hitler came to power in 1933. The father, Robert, was Germany's most distinguished statistician and demographer, and the British Committee for the Relief of the Victims of Fascism found him a three-roomed flat at 12 Lawn Road where his family soon joined him.

Ursula Kuczynski was born the year before Edith, but in Berlin, the second of six children. Like Edith, Ursula was a keen photographer. And Ursula, too, grew up surrounded by books and talk of revolution. She was an avid reader and had any text she desired within reach in her father's monumental library, one of the largest private collections in Germany. She read Reich and Max Gorky at a very early age, and they greatly influenced her political thinking. Books shaped her mind and traced her path. And first love came to Ursula, as it had to Edith, in an aisle of books, their smell suffusing the air, their possibilities and persuasions hidden tantalisingly beneath leather-bound covers.

And now Ursula's sister Brigitte is soon to move into the Lawn Road Flats with her husband, a member of the Communist Party who works for the BBC research department, while the rest of her family live down the road.

As they drink beer in the sunshine on the Flats' balcony, the Kuczynski family all want to hear about Ursula's life in Shanghai. She shows them photographs of Micha, her three-year-old son and her favourite subject, taken with a fifty-year-old Leica camera her husband gave her. Ursula is scathing about the women she was forced to spend time with in Shanghai. They had no profession and no interest in culture. They weren't even interested in their children or their household. So it was difficult for her to find common ground. She felt like an outsider, but she continued to play the part of mother and housewife.

Three years previous to the Lawn Road Flats opening, Ursula had married Rudolf Hamburger, an architect who would later also become a member of the Communist Party. They had immediately relocated to Shanghai where there was a huge amount of construction work going on and many opportunities for well-paid and innovative architectural works. There, Rudolf had designed the first modernist building in China, a nine-story apartment block for nurses' accommodation.

Ursula had written her beloved family plenty of letters over the previous years. She wouldn't risk severing that connection, no matter the distance or difficulty in maintaining contact. She'd told them of the Trans-Siberian Express – the week it took to get to the eastern border of the Soviet Union and then the further week on a Chinese train to Shanghai. Unlike the other foreigners, she'd travelled in second class and, denied access to the restaurant carriage, had prepared their meals with a spirit burner she'd brought, heating up soup day after day to save money. The landscapes had been sublime though – the majestic Lake Baikal shimmering into the distance, the endless expanse of the steppes. And when the train would grind to a halt, the passengers would stretch their legs and begin to dance arm in arm, jolly as could be.

She'd described life in the French concessionary quarter, a wealthy area where 48,000 foreigners resided and where the affluence was at odds with much of the rest of the city. She had told them of her attempts at learning Cantonese, of her pregnancy and the birth of her first child. She had sent photographs and written of falling head-over-heels with her little boy. She'd recounted integrating herself into the expat community, while feeling herself apart from them.

But it was what Ursula could not say that was of most importance to the family. Her parents knew she was more than a housewife and loving mother. Living double lives was par for the course in this family – almost all of them were at it to some degree. So they did not know the details of their oldest daughter's struggle but were well aware of the need to maintain a pretence of mediocrity. She worked for the GRU, after all.

There was so much she could not tell them. Until now.

Ursula's first and only real friend in Shanghai was a journalist named Agnes. The first time they met, Agnes was holding a bouquet of red roses in the Cathay Hotel café in the centre of Shanghai. Their meeting had been arranged, coincidentally, for the thirteenth anniversary of the Russian Revolution.

Agnes was a composed and intelligent working-class woman. She gave the impression that she was confident

and to the point, and yet there was a hidden complex-
ity about her, Ursula thought as she sat down. Agnes's
features were striking but she wasn't at all pretty. But
there was something inviting about her, and Ursula had
a feeling they might understand one another.

From the moment these two women met, they
spoke freely. Agnes was in Shanghai as a journalist
for the German newspaper *Frankfurter Zeitung*. She
told Ursula how when she first arrived, the exclusive
American Club had given a reception in her honour.
She'd attended the party thinking she was going to
meet interesting Chinese personalities, but in fact was
told there were no Chinese members of the club – they
weren't allowed to set foot inside. On hearing this fact,
Agnes had immediately stood up and left the room,
refusing to accept such prejudice. Though employed by
an internationally recognised publication, from that
point on she had been considered a person of suspicion
and added to the Chinese watchlist.

Agnes's marvellous collection of English, Chinese
and German books was another sign that she and Ursula
might be like-minded. The two polyglots quickly became
close friends, and shortly after their first meeting Agnes
told Ursula that she would receive a visit from a German
expat named Richard Sorge, an agent for the GRU.

It was November 1930 and Ursula was pregnant when
Richard Sorge arrived alone at her house. He was a tall
man in his mid-thirties with chiselled features and lots
of thick and wavy hair. His blue eyes and dark lashes
made an already intense gaze irresistible, and Ursula
simply stood by the door, for a moment forgetting to
respond. She stared at his beautiful mouth for a little
too long before recalling what she was supposed to do.

'Please do come in,' she laughed. She moved away
from the door and gave him space to enter the house.
Agnes had said that he was a good-looking man and she
had not exaggerated.

Once inside and standing in her kitchen, he did not waste his words.

'I have heard you are interested in giving your support to our Chinese comrades and their struggle against this reactionary government. Are you ready?'

She said yes. Then Richard explained how she needed to be extremely careful about not leaking any information to her husband and to make sure her neighbours continued to believe her cover as an innocent expat and mother.

First and foremost, he made it clear that he needed to use a room in her flat for various meetings, even though she would not be asked to join them. He meant to gather all the group's underground members in a place that would never be suspected. Her husband Rudolf must not find out what was happening in his house while he was at the office.

The circumstances in China were more favourable to their work than back home and the law amenable to many of their activities, at least ostensibly. But at the same time the government of Chiang Kai-shek was adamant in its desire to root out Communists and actively collaborated with its European counterparts. So, although Communists may have been given the freedom to publish and protest, it was often merely the rope to hang themselves with. Communists were regularly sent to prison and in most cases they never came back.

The Chinese comrades had learned the art of partisanship from the Soviets, who also provided them with aid in Japanese-occupied Manchuria. Agnes's mission was to train these partisans and facilitate their communication, leading them towards taking action.

Soon Ursula was arranging meetings and storing secret information at the back of her kitchen cupboard. There were revolvers belonging to the Chinese Red Army in her house, and she made it clear to Richard that she was happy to go further. Communism was a cause she was willing to spend her life fighting for, at any risk.

One morning, after many months of clandestine gatherings, Richard approached Ursula after a meeting and asked, 'Would you like to come on a bike ride with me tomorrow?'

Ursula had given birth a few months earlier. Who would babysit? Would Rudolf find out? She had to ponder for a second before answering, 'That would be wonderful, Richard, I'd love to.'

They met the next day in the outskirts of Shanghai, not far from Ursula's house. The sun was shining and the weather already pleasantly warm with a slight breeze. Ursula was wearing wide-legged, high-waisted sailor pants with a shirt and a light jacket. Her shoes didn't look too sporty though. She had taken her time finding the right outfit.

As soon as Richard arrived, she elegantly straddled the bike. Her smile was overwhelming. Richard hardly had time to greet her, so childishly impatient was she to start the adventure.

Although it was her first time on a motorbike, she had no fear. The only problem was that she didn't know where to put her feet. Richard had to instruct her how to use the footrests and how to hold on to him. Once that was sorted, Ursula felt secure and tapped his shoulder signalling her readiness to go.

Richard enjoyed driving fast, but of course Ursula couldn't judge the velocity. All she knew was that it was absolutely thrilling. Was Richard driving like he usually did or testing her courage? Either way, Ursula was having the time of her life and screaming her head off: 'Faster, faster!'

She couldn't remember the last time something so fun had happened and once they stopped felt disappointed – she was already addicted to the speed and the company. The adrenaline running through her body made her very talkative and uninhibited; she was laughing and feeling light.

That ride had changed her life.

Richard was her first taste of this strange and delicious danger. Not those meetings in her house exactly, although they excited her, but the motorbike rides they would go on around the outskirts of Shanghai – that's where it started. She loved the uncertainty of not knowing what tomorrow would bring.

Ursula was responsible for scheduling the meetings and keeping safe a suitcase full of secret information. She knew she had to appear casual and not give Rudolf the impression that something out of ordinary was happening in their home.

One day though, Rudolf bumped into two of the Chinese comrades by accident. She had to assure her husband that they were only her Chinese language teachers, employed by the government at the Institute of Social Sciences.

She was well aware of the dangers but was still surprised to one day see the set of revolvers lying unconcealed in her kitchen. A trunk was open, and the weapons were spread all over the floor. Her eyes fixed on them and she found herself unable to speak. Had Rudolf seen?

He hadn't but a turning point nonetheless: she had been called into action. Richard asked her to pack her stuff and be ready to leave immediately. Ursula felt anxious, not least about the baby. Micha was underweight and fragile. She knew that outside the big cities no milk or powdered milk would be available, but fortunately she was still breast-feeding.

After waiting a fortnight, there was still no more news about her departure. This was not unusual. Uncertainty was part of the job. Ursula had to be ready to leave but at the same time ready to hide a fellow comrade in her house for weeks if things were to take a new direction. She had to be on her toes and ready to adapt to continuously changing scenarios. She knew that Richard would give her all the necessary information and no more.

But in this instance, the order to run never came.

Those years in Shanghai were difficult. Ursula missed her family and often felt she needed their support, but taking Micha to Germany was totally unrealistic.

Soon it became clear that her family would have to abandon their house outside Berlin and start a new life in exile. This is when they moved to Hampstead. The news of how Germany was changing had reached Ursula in Shanghai, and she was shocked to find out how little the working classes were able to hinder the rise of the Fascists.

It was devastating. Hitler's ascendence to power was rapidly changing the world. Even in China, the consequences were being felt. The Swastika fluttered over the German consulate in Shanghai, a disturbing marker of developments on the other side of the world. The Fascist regime was making headlines, but detailed information wasn't available. It was lucky that Rudolf's employers were English. An influx of German architects meant that there were many people looking for a position, but he was safe for now.

The China–Japan conflict was not ending for the foreseeable future, but on the other hand Chiang Kai-shek was enjoying success against the Reds. The Nanjing government seemed to be in control, enough at least to turn their attention to building infrastructure and securing the Yangtse region against floods.

Ursula spent a lot of time outside Shanghai. The climate was more favourable for Micha, and she enjoyed being in the wonderful villages getting to know the local people. She felt at home there with the welcoming locals and was awed by their sense of solidarity in the face of hardship.

Ursula and Agnes went on long walks every afternoon and admired the vast vistas of the Yangtze valley spread before them and the rim of the Hubei mountain range arching its back to shelter the tree-covered slopes beneath, the paths through which were known only to the Reds.

A week after the opening party, Edith's steps were quick and edgy as she approached Kim, who was waiting for her outside Marble Arch Tube station. She was wearing an off-white maxi-length dress and sandals with a blue and white polka dot foulard, while he smoked a pipe, dashing as always in a smart suit. He matched her pace as they began to walk, and when she hailed a taxi, he climbed in after her. She had told Kim that he was to follow her without questions or comment. They got out of the taxi near Victoria, walked for a bit in silence, then hailed another and headed in the direction of Queensway.

'Don't ever go straight to a meeting,' Edith told him quietly. 'For every step you make in the right direction, you must make a deviation or go back and find another path. Make sure also that no one is following you.'

He nodded, gripping his pipe without smoking it.

After a quarter of an hour, she asked the taxi to stop and they began to walk towards Ladbroke Grove Tube station. Edith looked around her before heading underground.

They waited casually on the platform for the Hammersmith and City line. Once the train arrived and the doors opened, they still waited. Only when everyone else was on board the train, at the last second did they hop in, the doors closing behind them.

To Kim's surprise, Edith then turned around, grabbed the handle and slid the door open to get back on to the platform they had left a second before. Edith looked around to see if anyone else had done the same. Nothing, so they walked calmly out of the underground station and immediately hopped on a bus.

'How long do we have to play this game for?' Kim whispered, but Edith ignored him. They finally got out of the bus and walked, making a few detours, to Regent's Park.

'Here we are,' she said as they arrived at the boating lake, three and a half hours after they'd first met at Marble Arch. Edith approached a man on a bench and motioned for Kim to sit down.

'Hello,' the man said in German, offering a firm handshake.

With that, Edith shot off like an arrow.

URSULA

To escape the heat in Shanghai, Ursula and Agnes took a trip to a summer resort at the top of Mount Lu in Jiujiang, 1,200 metres above sea level. Agnes went ahead to find a bungalow for them to stay in while Ursula travelled up the River Yangtse with Micha. Everywhere she looked there was poverty and damage caused by the river's floods and fluctuations. Beggars arrived whenever the boat stopped, and many houses were still half under water from the last time it had risen.

Once the journey by steamer had ended, the journey by road began, which wasn't in any way easier – a horrid expedition in an ancient bus that clung to the foot of the hills as rainwater sloughed down from above, making many of the roads impassable. Finally, Ursula and Micha stepped out of the bus and bought tickets for the final stage of the trip: a sedan chair waiting to be pulled up the hill by coolies. Convinced to embark, it was soon clear to Ursula that the strain of this was immense on their carriers, and she asked them to stop. She carried Micha in her arms and started to climb up the steep road. The whole journey had been one depressing scene of mass deprivation after another and left no doubt about the discrepancies between normal people and the country's elites. Ursula started to believe more than ever in the cause she fought for.

The house Agnes had found in the mountains was a simple wooden bungalow, but it became a sacred refuge where they felt protected and hidden as the China–Japan war raged below. Outside it seemed there was hardly any resistance from the Chinese, caught unprepared for the onslaught, and the provinces in Manchuria were taken with ease.

Spending time outside Shanghai was a blessing, and their rural life seemed far away from all political conflicts, within and without China, However. Ursula continued to support the cause, actively helping to organise the revolutionary forces that fought the Japanese along the Manchurian border.

A few weeks after their arrival, Soong Chiang-Ling, a Chinese friend, was also supposed to join them. She was the widow of Sun Yat-sen, the revolutionary Chinese statesman and political philosopher who had served as the first president of the Republic of China. Since her husband's death, Soong Chiang-Ling had moved further and further to the left. Her life was complicated, though, by her sister marrying Chiang Kai-shek himself, leader of the Republic of China and the Generalissimo of the National Revolutionary Army. Soong Chaing-Ling had been financially disowned by her family as a consequence of her political beliefs, and with such a complex life, Ursula assumed there was a valid reason why Soong couldn't join them in the end.

Other friends did join the trip as planned though, including Professor Othmer, a language specialist who could decipher ancient Chinese scripts. He was able to read and translate the inscriptions on old temples fluently for their collective enlightenment.

Everything went well until the last week of their stay, when Richard arrived with news about the arrest of two Swiss Communists. They had been sentenced to death in China, but he had managed to organise for their sentence to be reduced to imprisonment. This couple had a five-year-old son who would now be growing up without parents.

Over lunch one day, conversation became heated. Ursula proposed that she would like to adopt the son of the Swiss Communists, but Richard and Agnes both thought this was a bad idea. Agnes, oddly, seemed incensed at the mere suggestion of it from Ursula – tragic as it was, the fate of a child to whom they had no connection could not be allowed to jeopardise their greater goal.

The Swiss couple had recently begun a hunger strike in jail, and in solidarity Agnes said she felt unable to eat. Ursula replied that Agnes's hunger wasn't going to have any effect on the couple's cause and in response Agnes pushed back her chair and left the room.

After lunch, Ursula went for a short walk and when she came back, she found a short and precise note from Agnes on the table:

> It is now clear to me that your private life plays far too much of a role here and you don't possess the commitment, the willingness to sacrifice oneself, that makes a real revolutionary. I can't possibly stay here under these circumstances – I leave now for Shanghai.

Ursula could hardly believe such a small misunderstanding could end their close friendship. As the holiday came to an end, she just hoped that Richard did not feel the same way. It was his opinion that she cared most about.

That evening, Ursula and Rudolf had some guests over for dinner. Among them were a couple from Germany. Ursula was burning with curiosity about the situation there, but the couple weren't talkative at all, and Ursula was relieved when the dull conversation was interrupted by a phone call.

Ursula jumped at the chance of leaving the table and passing the bamboo-patterned curtain that separated the hallway from the dining room. Next to the phone was a beautiful picture of her family estate in Schlachtensee, always a reminder of her happy childhood.

'I tried to reach you all afternoon,' came Richard's voice. 'I wanted to tell you personally but since I couldn't get hold of you, I'll have to tell you on the phone: I'm leaving.'

These words were stones dropping into Ursula's heart. She was speechless. The immensity of the loss engulfed her. Richard was still on the phone, but Ursula was incapable of responding. She pulled a chair close to the receiver and let herself sink into it, devastated, before remembering the guests on the other side of the curtain. She wanted to stay hidden in her sadness but knew she had to put on a brave face. She went back to the table composed, and no one noticed anything.

EDITH

Edith was sitting by the window at Litzi's place in West Hampstead. They were both impatient to see Kim and hear about his interview with Arnold. It was getting late, and there was still no sign of him. They drank tea and tried to distract each other with memories of Vienna – their favourite coffee shops, old friends they'd not seen in years.

But finally Kim arrived looking distraught and dishevelled. He took a moment to breathe and digest everything that had just happened while Edith and Litzi waited, holding their breath, pretending to read.

When he finally began to talk, he confirmed that 'Otto' did have a role for him in the class struggle. The women expressed happiness, but Kim stopped them. It was not that easy.

This was not the role any of them had desired or expected. Instead, Otto wanted Kim to infiltrate the system from the inside. Kim had been asked to return to the privileged and superficial life that every fibre of his being yearned to reject. He had to become part of the system they all despised. Using his contacts in the British establishment, his impeccable upper-class manners and his status as the son of a wealthy conservative aristocrat, Kim had been asked to get a job as journalist and then ideally work as a diplomat or in the government.

If he took the assignment, the trajectory of his whole life would change.

'You would have to give up all your Leftist affiliations and Communist friends,' Litzi said.

He nodded, staring at her as their future together crumbled around them. A desperate expression clouded her soft features.

After dinner, Kim sat in an armchair and lit his pipe. Edith got out the Rolleiflex from her bag and took a series of pictures in the semi-darkness: the pensive Kim with his head slightly inclined to the left, picturing himself on a voyage he had already embarked upon.

The next week Edith went to visit Jack and Molly at Lawn Road and deliver some pictures she'd taken for them. First, she had tea with her sister-in-law Beatrix, while Jennifer, her daughter with Jack, did puzzles at their feet. Beatrix worked at a progressive boarding school called Beacon Hill, founded by Bertrand Russell and his wife Dora, an advocate for Bolshevism and free love, two causes that Beatrix shared. A photo of Beatrix, Jack and Jennifer sat on the table, alongside one of Beatrix, Jack and Jack's wife, Molly, having a picnic on the beach.

This was the first time Edith had been inside one of the flats since the opening, when it was alive with the thrum of conversation and the tinkling of glasses and laughter. Beatrix and her daughter lived in one of the twenty-two 'minimum' flats, only 269 square feet each but ideally proportioned and functional, self-sufficient with every need considered. Beatrix spoke of the architects, artists, writers and politicians who had started to move into the building, along with political refugees from the Fascist regimes. It was thrilling.

Beatrix and Jennifer took Edith up to the penthouse where Molly and Jack lived. Together they looked at Edith's work spread out upon the table, images of the sunny day not long past when the public had gathered to welcome this alien object to their tranquil streets.

The flats had been lauded in every architectural magazine, and Molly and Jack could not have asked for more. The one minor irritation was that Wells Coates, still Molly's lover, had become upset at the suggestion, made by certain sections of the press, that the building's design belonged to the clients rather than him, the architect. Molly had given the brief to Wells Coates and felt very proud of it.

Molly and Jack's penthouse flat was a slightly bigger version of Beatrix's, though the south-facing roof terrace was larger than the flat itself. The walls were birch-veneer, and the chequerboard timber floors the colour of maple syrup. The room they sat in was both a dining and reception area, and from it you could see into the bedroom, with its built-in wardrobes and wooden panelling.

After an hour going over the photographs with Molly and Beatrix, Edith went grocery shopping and then for a walk on Hampstead Heath, where she found Arnold sitting on a bench near the ponds, as expected. Edith's face lit up as soon as she saw him, but she took a deep breath, trying to disguise any excitement. Once she arrived, they began to walk together, pausing occasionally to look at the ducks or the children playing in the park.

They switched languages occasionally, from German to English and then back again. It was safer to speak in English, but she couldn't help it – she unconsciously searched for the closeness of their relationship in Vienna. But Arnold was very matter of fact, and all he was interested in was Kim's recruitment and how important a student from Cambridge could be for them. Edith searched for more between the lines, occasionally trying to speak of memories or feelings, but Arnold cut her off. The meeting had only lasted fifteen minutes when Arnold indicated it was time to part. He turned towards Edith with a cool smile.

'Well done,' he said. 'I have asked him to compile a list of any Cambridge peers of his who have the access and will to infiltrate establishment institutions.'

Arnold sat in the Marcel Breuer Long Chair of flat number 1 at 32 Lawn Road, its laminated birch wood surface curved so his weight could be distributed across it evenly, a feature of every living room. He would often lie back and listen to his favourite music: Brahms, Haydn, Beethoven, certainly not Wagner – a taste he shared with Edith. Their connection had opened many doors for him.

His wife Josephine was still in Moscow training as a secret-police radio operator, so the apartment was sparse and tidy, apart from the books piled on the floor, the table, the kitchen top and even on his bed. The flat's multifunctional book unit was placed against the wall and was also, of course, full of books. Arnold liked these units because he could stack and organise the way he needed. The ingenious piece of furniture, its shelves formed to hold the Penguin paperbacks that had democratised reading, was designed by the architect Egon Riss, another tenant. It was the first commercial product to be sold and used beyond the Isokon building.

The idea behind the flats and their furniture was that the tenants would be given exactly the space they needed to be comfortable but no more. The bed was a sofa bed, at an angle to his book unit. By the window there was a comfortable armchair where Arnold sat quite often. And facing this was a Marcel Breuer tubular table and two chairs, where he would read his students' papers most evenings.

Arnold was an academic and had taken a position at the London University. This was his cover. His flat was on the ground floor, which he preferred for discreet access. It didn't have much light, except in the kitchen area where a window opened up straight to the main entrance, allowing some rays of sunshine to infiltrate the inside.

Full of Left-wing, openminded residents, it was the perfect base for Arnold. There were a number of BBC employees, and occasionally Arnold would bump into them in the Isobar – the club belonging to the building, a half-hundred club where its twenty-five members were allowed one guest at a time.

Arnold didn't often use the numerous services that were offered – bed-making, clothes-washing, window-cleaning and dusting, meals being sent to each apartment. He didn't like people coming in and out of his flat, discovering his routines and getting to know more about him. Nevertheless, the set-up at Lawn Road allowed him to meet up with different people in a casual, inconspicuous way.

Brigitte was in her flat writing to her sister, looking out on the woodland beyond. She could feel a train rumble on in the distance as she sat on her Marcel Breuer chair.

Ursula always provided the minimum amount of information necessary, so it was important to read between the lines. Their letters were of children and quotidian life, recipes and weather and books they had read. Nothing of note to the uninitiated, but if you knew where to look there was little that went unexpressed. They loved reading each other's letters, arguing about Gorky, Marx, Russell, filling their pages with quotes and underlining. 'To fear love is to fear life, and those who fear life are already three parts dead,' Ursula had quoted Bertrand Russell in her previous letter, from his 1929 book *Marriage and Morals*. Brigitte wondered what part of her sister's marriage or morals might be being hinted at.

Edith opened the back door to the Brixton house. Litzi, in a good mood, smiled at her friend and followed her downstairs into the humid basement. Edith hadn't been feeling very well that morning but put it down to anxiety.

Ten minutes later Kim arrived, and Edith showed him too down to the basement. There was a sad, strange quiet in the air that day. Edith closed the door to give them some privacy.

Litzi and Kim were not meant to meet any more, but they snuck into Edith's basement once a week, which she had tried her best to make cosy with a mattress and fresh flowers. It was still dark and damp though. As soon as the couple saw each other they embraced, letting the familiar touch take the place of politics and fear. There was hardly any light downstairs except a small chink below the ceiling leading toward the street, and after they made love they lay in this quiet dark and watched passersby and their parade of shoes: brogues, boots, heels. In the rainy autumn weather some shoes had leaves stuck to their soles. There was so much going through Litzi's head as she tried to imagine herself and a future without Kim. She didn't know what was to become of their relationship.

The next week, when Litzi arrived for their rendezvous, she told Edith that Kim would not be joining them. He had got a job at *The Times* through his father's connections and was going to report on the Spanish Civil War. With this perfect cover, they hoped he would be able to pass on important information to Litzi. Code named Mary, Litzi would be sent to Paris, from where she would meet Kim whenever possible in Biarritz, Perpignan or Gibraltar to receive his reports and then forward them on to Moscow.

Edith often went for tea or drinks at Lawn Road with Molly and Beatrix, sitting in the penthouse and looking out on to the train tracks and streets. These friends could not quite fill the void left by Litzi's absence, but they tried. Molly and Beatrix comforted Edith when her father died, when her relationship with Alexander was difficult and when she realised she was pregnant.

Edith had watched the building fill up, and a year after the opening, all the flats were occupied. Edith occasionally passed Brigitte Kuczynski in the corridor. Walter Gropius, founder of the Bauhaus school, moved in after fleeing Nazi Germany, and two of his fellow Bauhaus masters came with him – László Moholy-Nagy, a graphic designer and photographer, and Marcel Breuer. Writers, translators, broadcasters, exiles, all came to Lawn Road Flats. And, of course, Arnold Deutsch.

It was easy for Edith to visit her friends and then duck down to knock on Arnold's door, hidden by the staircase on the ground floor for this purpose, where he would be marking papers while sitting on his Long Chair, books and notes scattered across the tubular table. Arnold was always busy, and kept a deliberately unpredictable schedule, but Edith was welcome to slip in and pass on the occasional document or piece of information, even when Josephine was there. Everything was professional now.

URSULA

Ursula was never contacted by Richard after his departure to Moscow, but she heard indirectly of him. He must have dropped a few good words about her to the Red Army Intelligence, which resulted in further developments. One day, their mutual friends in Shanghai asked her to consider going to Moscow for a six-month training period.

The condition was, however, that Ursula would go alone – without her son. She watched Micha, now two years old, playing on the floor with some wooden toys gifted by Chinese friends of Ursula, and started to think. His smooth forehead furrowed with concentration at arranging the toy figures to his taste, Ursula had a sudden sadness at the sight of him so sheltered in his own universe.

She went through potential scenarios in her head. She couldn't possibly take him to her parents, just now preparing to emigrate to England. Perhaps it would be better to stay with Rudolf's family in their chalet on the Czech side of the Riesengebirge mountain chain close to the German border. But she would need an excuse for this imposition. She would have to argue that it was all for the health of Micha. And it wouldn't be too unheard of; many of the foreigners living in China sent their wives and children to Europe for long stays – perhaps it would be good for him ... She tried in vain to convince herself, but the void was eating her from the inside knowing the grief that would accompany their separation. She stooped and took him in her arms, squeezing him as though for the last time, hot tears dampening her cheeks.

Ursula and Micha looked back at the receding Shanghai skyline as the ship departed the harbour, the silhouettes of the port's two bulk cargo terminals looming large in the foreground in front of the ridged back of high-rises that made up the international city. Nostalgia grew in Ursula even as the skyline was slowly claimed by the distant haze. She thought of the many comrades left behind in Shanghai and Manchuria, certain to face increasing danger. When would they return?

Ursula and Misha were not welcome on board the ship. It was a Norwegian freighter and not made to take passengers. The First Officer was not pleased at having to give up his cabin, and the rest of the crew barely spoke to them. All their meals were served separately, and to combat the isolation Ursula invented stories and read books to Micha so he didn't get bored.

The days were beautiful and sunny, the timber loaded on board germinating a fabulous scent that spread around the boat. Ursula tried not to think of the separation she was facing, knowing she would miss half a year of Micha's development.

The plan to have Micha stay with Rudolf's parents in their Czech mountain chalet had been settled on. They believed Ursula's story – that she was planning to move to the Soviet Union merely because Germany was out of question. Ursula's mother was going to join them since her life in Germany was becoming more and more miserable, while her father had already moved to England to look for a job. Ursula was thrilled to show her mother her first grandchild.

Upon her arrival in Moscow, Ursula was fetched by an officer and brought directly to Hotel Novaya Moskovska. Ursula was told she had a new name now: Sonya.

She felt immediately at ease with this new persona.

The separation from Micha was painful though. Her body had ached with it when she dropped him at her parents-in-law in Czechoslovakia. Fortunately she was not going to have much time on her own, with the training due to begin straight away.

The same officer who picked her up from the boat was due to pick her up from the hotel the next morning and accompany her to the training centre in Arbat. She barely slept, missing Micha in the night, and so was up and dressed early. She entered the elevator at the fifth floor, where her room was located, and pushed the button for the lobby.

But as she waited there a hand tapped her shoulder and she jumped, not expecting anyone in Moscow to know her except Richard. This time a wonderful surprise befell her: she turned her head and there was Agnes.

Their falling out was forgotten now, and they started seeing each other as a matter of routine. Ursula would drop by for supper each Saturday, and the next morning they would have breakfast with Borodin, whom they knew very well from China.

Borodin was chief editor of the English-language weekly *Moscow News*. Those breakfast meetings turned out to be fascinating hours. They mostly spoke about China, which was Agnes's field of expertise. Agnes was even asked to write a book about children in the Red Provinces.

Agnes then asked Ursula to write it for her since she was too busy. Ursula agreed and the manuscript got accepted by the publisher, who decided to print it with photographs that Agnes and Ursula had taken in China.

Of course, all the activities Ursula undertook outside the school were meticulously surveilled, and the school was aware of her meetings with Agnes and Borodin.

Ursula's time was packed, and she had hardly a moment to think. That is until one day she was asked to talk to the major of the Red Army.

Ursula had no idea what to expect as she entered the major's office and was asked to take a seat in front of his desk. He sat immobile opposite her, a still life behind the table, formidable, his chest festooned with decorations, a stern expression seemingly frozen on his face.

Ursula felt intimidated and hardly looked at him as she took the seat she was offered and waited. Silence filled the room. Ursula could feel his eyes examining her body language, trying to uncover her character through observation, but she barely moved. To break the ice, the major stood up and came towards her.

'Can you tell me your life story – in Russian?'

Ursula was taken aback and didn't know if her abilities were up to the task. Still, she had to give it a try.

To her own surprise, she managed to tell him the story quite eloquently.

Ursula had passed the test, and she was on the way to her next mission with a new partner chosen for her by Moscow. The man was named Ernst, a sailor from working-class beginnings who had completed the same course at the Centre. The destination was a city called Mukden in China, known as the Siberia Station in the inner circle. It was a Soviet Tomis, an exile at the end of the earth.

They arrived separately in Prague. Ursula was on her way to pick up Micha from his grandparents' house in the mountains but would first stay overnight in Prague. Ernst invited her to go to the cinema with him to watch a French film called *Maternelle*, the leading roles played by children.

When they arrived the cinema was already almost full, but they managed to find two seats at the front. Ursula had been thrilled with the idea and thought it a good way to take her mind off Micha. Halfway through the movie, though, she had tears in her eyes. What had seemed to be a good idea turned out to be bitterly stressful. She missed Micha tremendously. She was unable to hide her emotions although she had tried hard, not wanting to give the impression of being weak. Ursula quickly wiped her tears away, hoping that Ernst had not noticed in the dark. But he had, and he put his arms around her shoulder to help calm her. Ursula felt his warmth and protection.

Once they came out of the theatre, Ernst asked if she would like to come to a café for a drink. Ursula's eyes were red and stinging, but she accepted his kind offer.

To her surprise, he didn't bombard her with questions about her private life. On the contrary, he started to tell the story of his own family.

'I was the son of a fisherman in Hamburg. His money was mostly spent on drink. My mother had to work and earn money to support all four children on her own.'

'What a hero she was, to give you an education despite all that.'

'For me it was painful to witness how my father treated my mother, and after a while I decided to leave the family and search for a new life on my own. So I became a sailor. That was not a lifestyle that suited me though, and I ended up on my own a great deal. While my mates went out and played cards and relaxed in the harbour, I read books on Marxist philosophy.'

Ernst, Ursula and Micha travelled together from Prague to Trieste, then via the Suez Canal on to Bombay and Singapore and Hong Kong. Ursula and Ernst would meet at night, leaning over the ship's rail, whispering to each other or watching the dark expanse of water churn below. In Ursula's mind things were certainly evolving, albeit not in the way she had planned.

Before they made the last stretch of their journey, Ursula and Ernst stopped in Shanghai. Rudolf was expecting their arrival and had been looking forward to it with unease: she had already warned him that they had something important to discuss. Better to do it in person rather than in a letter from far away, she thought.

And upon their arrival, she did not take long to tell him what was on her mind: she wanted a separation. Rudolf was crushed at the thought of being far away from their son and insisted that they all stay close and connected despite agreeing to the divorce she wished for.

Preparations for Mukden began. Ursula was going as the representative of the Shanghai Evans & Co bookshop and obtained written confirmation to allay any suspicions. This would be her cover.

The Japanese war and the ascent of Nazis in Germany had finally brought Rudolf closer to Ursula's views. He was more understanding than ever about the situation Ursula had committed herself to. One day Ursula walked into her living room and was baffled to see Rudolf and Ernst kneeling on the living room floor removing the padding from a large armchair that had just been delivered.

Ernst had asked for Rudolf's help in transporting a transformer to Mukden. It was a heavy iron block that measured eight inches square. It wouldn't exactly fit in their luggage, so he had the brilliant idea to hide it just inside the armchair. Ursula watched them as they gutted it, working together. 'It will be quite normal for you to take furniture from your house in Shanghai to Mukden,' Rudolf said proudly.

They secured the transformer with one more piece of tough string at the end and then nailed the fabric back on to the base of the chair.

Ursula and Ernst arrived in Mukden and checked in to their room. There, Ursula purposely left the letter from Evans's bookshop lying around, along with Ernst's letter of recommendation. Any snoopers would discover this immediately. And as a further precaution, they never exchanged a word about their work when in the hotel.

Their mission was to find and meet with the partisans resisting the Japanese invasion in Manchuria. These partisan groups had been formed in the villages and mountains, where Japanese control was weakest, and were led by Communists. The idea was to reach out to them and assist their efforts to disrupt Japanese communication and operations in industrial areas.

The transmitter that Ursula and Ernst were installing would enable the partisans to have direct contact with the Soviet Union – a way of submitting questions as well as passing on information and reports.

Ernst assumed they would move in to a house together in Mukden, but Ursula wasn't in favour of this idea. She wanted to keep her privacy without having to accommodate Ernst. They were both strong-minded people who liked things done their way, which Ursula knew would create conflict.

So Ernst found a room with a German couple who were in need of money, and they started to look for a place for Ursula and Micha. This wasn't an easy task since most of the empty properties were taken by the Japanese officials – only a few luxurious villas remained on the market, all of them abandoned by Chinese generals.

Their first viewing started with a villa that belonged to a relation of General Zhang Xue-liang, who had ruled the region until the Japanese invasion. Two animals carved from black stone watched over the house from plinths at the entrance.

This house was too ostentatious for Ursula's needs, but on the way out of the grounds she stopped by a small garden cottage. The servant smiled and with a twinkle in his eye and confidential tone explained that this house was used by the general for his mistresses. There was a secret passageway underground connecting it to the villa.

'Would it be possible to have a look?' Ursula enquired.

The servant was hesitant but went to find the keys. The little garden house comprised three small rooms, all covered with beautiful painted wooden panels. The kitchen was built into the basement next to the servants' quarters, the perfect place for a tunnel linking the houses.

Ursula thought the setting would be ideal for her work. The windows all had shutters that could be locked from the inside, and it was well hidden at the back of the garden, so relatively private. There was a couch in one of the rooms that could be turned into a bed for Ursula. Additionally, Ursula would be allowed to choose some other furniture from the main villa, and it was a bargain, the equivalent of just thirty shillings a month.

Soon after Ursula moved in, the transmitter arrived in its chair and Ernst started to build and install it. All the material looked rather bulky: large valves, heavy copper tubing coils that turned around a beer bottle. There was also the Morse key that had two rulers, one made out of brass for the Chinese characters and another out of wood. Moving a wooden cotton reel brought the bolt out from the centre and it hit the metal ruler. The art was that the key had to be mounted and dismounted as fast as possible.

The installation was demanding, but Ernst was up to the task. Searching for the perfect spot, he ended up lowering the transmitter and rectifier into a camphor chest they had brought from Shanghai and fitting it all under a wooden desk. A perfect set-up, and one that would not be easy for the police to locate.

The messages were sent to someone from the Red Army in Vladivostok but finding the wavelength was a challenge each time. Although the messages Ursula sent were never too long, it took several hours for them to go through because of the jamming of the system. It was equally strenuous getting the messages back from Russia. And then there was the next hurdle – deciphering the coded dispatches.

She was very careful and operated at night while her son was deep asleep. She first closed all the windows and shutters, and then turned off all the lights except for the small lamp on her desk. In the inky night, the house looked like a dark fortress.

Ursula found the work in Mukden exciting and unpredictable. She did not have friends, but that was no problem. The surest way to avoid betrayal, she believed, was to give people the minimum amount of information.

One day though, a comrade was recommended by the Centre. His name was Li and their encounters became regular. Ernst and Ursula trusted him. It was always a poker game, judging if people were reliable or not. The truth was that one's character was only revealed when danger threatened. That was the ultimate test.

Ursula enjoyed excursions to the city of Fushun. This was reached by a stunning two-hour train ride from Mukden through mountains swathed in the deep green foliage of ancient trees, their slopes falling away dramatically into precipitous gorges. The walled city from the Ming Dynasty had been transformed into the industrial centre of Manchuria, and as the train wound its way in through the outskirts, Ursula reflected on complete contrast of this modernised conurbation to its mountainous surrounds – under the governance of another power. She took pictures along the way documenting how landscapes and silhouettes tell the stories of places.

Ernst and Ursula were asked by the Centre not to contact any Japanese during their excursions, but nevertheless they found opportunities to speak to some.

Everything was planned. Ursula and Ernst went out to get all the material they needed to build the explosives. They had a shopping list of things that were not dangerous per se. Only in combination with other elements would they become a threat. So they pushed Micha's pram around the shops like any other family out shopping. Sugar, maybe for a cake. Potassium chlorate, maybe for a firework party. Hydrochloric acid, maybe to develop photos.

They entered a hardware store and asked the shopkeeper in stilted Chinese if he had ammonium nitrate.

This was used as a fertiliser as well as in explosives. The only problem was that Ursula couldn't define the quantity in Chinese. She tried her luck, and they ended up receiving a massive amount of the stuff, as if they were planning on starting an entire farm. Ursula realised that despite all her efforts at learning Chinese daily, it wasn't enough. She must work harder.

The ammonium nitrate was the key ingredient. Mixed with sugar or aluminium powder in the right ratio, this would produce a very effective bomb. They loaded up the pram until it was quite full, and then left for Ursula's place.

Meanwhile, the Japanese were taking over the city, constructing large new urban districts and new governmental buildings. They were slowly replacing all the Europeans goods, driving the European merchants to bankruptcy and swamping the markets with their own products. The result was that, between drought and flood, famine settled over the region. The Japanese called the partisans who rebelled bandits. These rebels would sometimes carry out more than 650 attacks a month.

One day the Centre contacted Ursula to say that a man had been arrested with a typewriter whose serial number corresponded to her own Rhein-Metall model. She had absolutely not sold it to this man, but danger hovered. The orders were strict: Ursula had to leave immediately and go straight to the Soviet Union. Ernst had to stay behind and, if questioned, would blame the sale on Ursula. This hasty plan of departure provoked a storm. Rudolf came immediately from Shanghai to meet her.

Once Ursula was aware of the news, she felt torn. It meant a separation from Ernst, and she had a secret she had not shared with him yet.

Before her departure she had to make a decision about the child she was carrying. It would be easy in her profession, and especially in China, to arrange an abortion, but was it what she wanted? Micha was four years old, so it was a good time to have a second child. And there would always be something in the way. She might never meet anyone she was as attracted to as Ernst.

With all this running through her head, she ultimately decided it was best to keep the child and announce it to Ernst and Rudolf at some point before her departure. They both tried to dissuade her, but Ursula was not sure what the future might hold – she might never become pregnant again.

Ursula went to her room and started to pack. Sitting on the edge of the bed, she looked at herself in the mirror: do you really know what you are doing?

She reflected on her life and the uncertainties that greeted her. What is real – what is really, truly real and what false? But she knew what she wanted, and no matter how difficult it was to follow her instinct, she had to pursue her convictions in work and in life. Whatever the future held in store, she was going to have a second child with her lover and would separate from him and leave for Moscow. The next day she boarded the train with Micha.

Once Ursula arrived in Moscow, she was greeted warmly by her good friend and comrade, Andrei: 'You have lost a lot of weight since last we met! What was that, a year and a half?'

The conversation turned to Mukden and the details of her work there. But once they'd caught up and she had been thoroughly debriefed, Andrei shocked her by requesting she go to Poland with Rudolf.

'I agree to go,' said Ursula after a pause, 'but Rudolf should decide for himself.' The idea of living with him again was no longer attractive. But she was unable to explain to Andrei about Ernst. Ultimately, she never was free to choose who she'd live with in her work.

Before she departed, she was given a small ceremony and received the Order of the Red Banner, the highest award possible, for her outstanding espionage work in China, and now ranked equal to a colonel in the Soviet military. Ursula left Moscow for Leningrad, and from there began a five-day journey by steamer to visit her family in England, her one condition on taking the post.

When she arrived and stepped along the eggshell walkway of the Isokon, she was not the only pregnant spy in residence. Had Edith and Ursula known their lives were barrelling down their tracks in parallel, hurtling through tunnels and over mountains, maybe they would have stopped to chat. They might have befriended one another, joined streams to form a single flowing river. And when they both had children, they might have swapped tips on how to perform spycraft while attending to a screaming toddler. Or on how to use a pram as a disguise. But no such meeting was ever documented.

Ursula and Brigitte Kuczynski had not seen each other for a while and so they chatted and laughed as they walked quickly from Brigitte's place to where the whole family was waiting for them in their parents' flat just down the road.

All the siblings were there, some with their partners, along with their nanny, Olga, who had looked after them from birth. The children called her Ollo. She had stayed at their house in Berlin after her employers emigrated, but she could not bear to be separated from the family long and soon joined everyone in London.

The family used to live in south-west Berlin in a magnificent house with gardens leading down the Schlachtensee lake. They had brought hardly any possessions to London, and yet their small three-bedroom flat was jammed with books, papers and paintings. Her father's desk was overflowing with meticulous notes for his upcoming book on population fluctuations, their economic consequences.

Something delicious was cooking in the kitchen. Berta was preparing a stew with meat and vegetables. The smell reminded Ursula of her childhood in Schlachtersee, when her mother would leave the *Tafelspitz* to slowly roast and their appetite would grow until it felt endless.

Ursula had been dreaming of this moment in Shanghai: the love, the conversation, the shared ideals.

The first thing that Ursula announced once the hugs and hellos had been dealt out was that she was pregnant. She wanted to get that news out of the way so she could enjoy the rest of the dinner.

Her parents were perplexed. They couldn't understand why she would choose to have a second child when she already had so much trouble raising Micha around her frequent trips. And they didn't think it was an ideal political moment to have children, with all the uncertainty surrounding the status of immigrants. Brigitte, though, was more understanding and expressed a lot of joy – especially for Micha, who desperately wanted a little brother or sister. And who knew when she would have another chance to give him one? She neglected to mention that the baby was not her husband's biological child, although he had agreed to raise it as if it were.

Over the Kuczynski dinner table, Brigitte offered her sister a quiet smile of understanding while the family continued doling out food and talking, with quick wit and sensitivity, about the escalating global problems. The family comprised six siblings, their two partners and their mother, who was the sun around which the whole family revolved, the centre of all conversation – something spouses usually found difficult at first. But it was thanks to Berta that the siblings contained within each one of them a deep sense of security. Nanny Ollo, too, had been a vital support at all times.

As conversation flowed freely at the table, Ursula was overcome by an urgent need to tell someone the truth and seized the chance to take her brother Jürgen to one side and speak to him alone. In the corridor she took his hand and whispered that the child she was expecting was not her husband's. Jürgen didn't want to believe it, but he showed understanding by squeezing her in his arms, which meant a lot to Ursula – to be forgiven, at least.

When Ursula returned to Poland she brought Ollo with her, which proved her undoing. Five years later, as war exploded across Europe, this woman would denounce her.

EDITH

Edith gave birth to a son, Tommy, and was suddenly divided in ways she had never experienced before. She was a mother, a spy, a wife. She knew that she had to stay more focused than ever now that the stakes were so high – any kind of professional mishap might endanger her family.

One morning, Alexander casually told her he was planning to go to Spain to join the Civil War as a surgeon in the International Brigades. Edith was speechless. What about their marriage? What about their son? What about her work? He claimed it would be just for a few months, but she knew her husband better than that. He needed to feel important – he needed to feel part of a great struggle and would find that need better satisfied in Spain than here in their little house with a screaming baby. In his mind he would be of greater use over there, helping the people resist Fascism.

'I will send money whenever I am able. That should help you take care of Tommy,' he told her, and then tried to make her feel selfish for putting herself above her cause: he argued that the class struggle between dictatorship and republican democracy, between Fascism and Communism, took precedence over family life. This war was exposing political divisions across Europe, and the outcome would dictate the sociopolitical landscape of the world.

Before Tommy was born, Edith would have agreed. Now, holding her baby in her arms, she was shocked by the coldblooded way Alexander was speaking. He was not just leaving for these grandiose reasons, and that was the truth. He was also leaving because their son cried constantly, to the extent that doctors were wondering if there was something wrong with him. He was leaving because they weren't having sex anymore, and because he was jealous of Arnold. He was also leaving because he was addicted to opium. He claimed to want to change the world but would not face the changes required of himself.

It was as if another Alexander had revealed himself after Tommy was born. There was the man she knew from before, the man who took her to the rally in Trafalgar Square, who wrote her endless letters signed with kisses, who married her in Vienna to help her escape jail. Then there was this secretive, brutal man who had no regard for her feelings.

Edith missed Litzi and wished they could be companions once more.

URSULA

In Poland, Ursula gave birth to a baby girl. With the rising tide of Fascism, Ursula knew she now had so much more to lose and to fight for. Outside her hospital window, demonstrators marched past the windows.

When she got home, she seemed the picture of domestic bliss. Micha was thrilled to have a little sister for company and very affectionate with her from day one. He enjoyed holding her and observing her, being her big brother, her protector. She was christened Nina, in a church as required by the State, and the three of them began a happy life together.

But the Swastika was hanging from ever more official and unofficial buildings, and when she walked her children in the park, she saw signs banning Jews from entering. Ursula had already made contact with a group of six comrades, all based in Danzig. Her mission was to assemble as much information possible about the Nazis' predicted invasion and then help prepare a campaign against it.

Danzig was a hub of activity. Armaments were transported from there to the civil war in Spain and U-boats were made in the shipyard. All the industrial production of the city was working in aid of the Fascist regimes. Ursula knew that any disruption, even as small as destroying traffic junctions, would be a tremendous help.

Ursula sent photos of the baby back to Lawn Road and Brigitte tucked them into the corner of the Bauhaus pictures framed on her walls. They grow so fast at that age, she thought, grateful to have this window on to her niece as she developed.

Nina was a beautiful little girl.

EDITH

Brigitte had a date at the Isobar. As she walked down the stairs she said hello to Edith, who was pushing a pram with a sleeping child inside.

'I'm not sure we've ever been formally introduced,' said Brigitte, offering her hand. 'I feel like we pass each other in the corridors constantly, but we've never said hello.'

'Edith,' she replied with a tired smile.

'Brigitte. You take beautiful photos. I've seen them in Molly's flat.'

'Thank you.'

'Can I help with the pram? Are you going to see Molly?'

Together, Edith and Brigitte went up the stairs with the pram, and then Brigitte continued on back down with a wave.

Downstairs, the kitchen had been converted into a small restaurant. Designed by Marcel Breuer, this basement area was offered to artists as an exhibition space and a place for the community to hold events and invite friends and colleagues. It regularly held themed lunches, one of which was taking place that day to fundraise for medical aid in Spain.

It was busy in the Isokon dining room. A wall-sized map of Hampstead hung at the far end next to a well-equipped bar bordered by Alvar Aalto stools. The room was functional yet cozy.

Brigitte was meeting Allan Foote, an attractive car mechanic, for lunch. He had recently returned from Spain where he'd fought with the International Brigades.

Taking in the room, he raised one eyebrow and gave Brigitte a slow, ironic smile. Allan was clearly amused by the refined surroundings he found himself in, as well as his evidently privileged middle-class contact. They both ordered *Fideos a la Cazuela*, a Catalan clay-pot chicken and noodle dish, and spoke of Spain, and London. Then Brigitte passed over a ten-pound note and details of how to contact Ursula in Switzerland, where she had recently moved with her husband and two children. Ursula was now working as a specialist radio operator and was establishing a group of anti-Fascist activists prepared for dangerous work inside Germany. Allan Foote would be one of them.

With her husband now gone, Edith turned to children's photography to make some money. She left their house in Brixton and moved to Maida Vale. In all her letters she expressed her wish to see Alexander and described how important it was for Tommy to spend time with his father. She was even ready to travel to Spain with Tommy if it was too difficult for him to get back. She continuously told him that she and Tommy loved him but got nothing in return.

And the civil war raged on. Soon after the destruction of Guernica, a few thousand Basque refugees arrived in England and were mainly accommodated in Brighton and North Stoneham, a village near Southampton. Edith visited Stoneham and took pictures of the adolescent refugees playing cricket with English boys. She shared these experiences with her colleague, Vera, who worked at the same studio and had been courageous in documenting the International Brigades and the horrors of war, receiving global recognition. This experience had taken its toll, and it was clear to Edith that Vera's physical and mental health was deteriorating rapidly. When Beatrix put on a joint show of their wartime photography in the building, Vera was too weak to attend.

Edith's letters remained unanswered, and it was only through Litzi that Edith learnt that Alexander was in a hospital sixty kilometres from Zaragoza. Litzi knew this because Kim was lucky enough to have survived an explosion – a Russian one, ironically – while in a car with three other English journalists and had ended up in the same place. Kim was the only survivor.

As the war continued apace, news was dripping in from Russia of Stalin's campaign to strengthen his power over the Communist Party. The NKVD, the secret police of the USSR, were charged with eradicating Stalin's rivals. What became known as the 'purges' began inside the government but quickly expanded to the military, and then further, with terrifying speed, to civilians suspected to be saboteurs or counterrevolutionaries. The NKVD used imprisonment, torture, violent interrogation and random executions to maintain control over the masses. Nobody knew who to trust, or what ideology was worth this level of danger and brutality.

Even the staunchest followers of the Communist regime started to ask questions about the fate of all those who had dedicated themselves to the cause and yet were disappearing by the hand of the very same system.

When Arnold was called back to Moscow, Edith feared the worse for him, Josephine and their little daughter. So many of their mutual friends, suspected of being enemies of Stalin's regime, were said to have been arrested and purged to the Gulags. An atmosphere of uncertainty reigned in Moscow, but also in England: no one was protected. It truly was an unsettling period.

Edith took a self-portrait with the camera Arnold had given her all those years ago in Vienna, when her idealism had been so pure. It was like looking at a different woman. Head tilted downwards, dressed modestly in a grey jumper, she sat on a chair, not facing the camera, but at an angle with a cigarette in her left hand. She cleverly concealed her other hand beneath her elbow in order to press the shutter button. Her expression was melancholic. She did nothing to hide the exhaustion apparent in the shadows under her eyes.

Edith was astounded by the image. She had not admitted to herself how difficult her life had become. Without words, this portrait described everything about her inner state of mind. The woman in this photograph wants to tell a story. It's as if she not only carries the burdens of the past, but those yet to come.

She decided to show it to Beatrix to express the loneliness she was going through.

Edith left her studio on 158 Haverstock Hill with the picture in an envelope and walked towards Lawn Road. As she approached, the afternoon sun cut the Isokon building in two. She wished she'd brought her camera to capture the beautiful shadows that patterned its side.

That day Molly invited Edith to a farewell party she'd organised for Marcel Breuer, planned for the coming Christmas Eve. 'Come as a guest, not as a photographer,' she said. Molly knew Edith would enjoy meeting the Bauhaus master and his wife, along with many others in the private circle of twenty or so that would be attending. The Breuers had become good friends of the Pritchards, who had made great efforts to find more commissions for Marcel. But as job opportunities for architects were scarce, the Breuers had decided to emigrate to the United States on the advice and encouragement of their friend and colleague, Walter Gropius, who had left for Massachusetts a year earlier.

'Thank you Moll, it would be an honour to join,' said Edith.

It was freezing cold on the 24th of December 1937. The damp scent of winter was in the air, the street lamps illuminating the early evening gloom. Hampstead was in a fog, and Edith was walking the short distance from her studio fast in order to keep warm. She wore a brown mohair coat with a high velvet collar over a long black woollen dress that showed underneath, shielding her legs from the cold. Her hat and thick scarf were geometrically patterned, in dark tones as was her style, not being a fan of colour. Although she was tempted to take her camera, she had followed Molly's orders and left it behind.

She arrived a little late. As she entered the Isobar, she noticed the barograph hanging on the wall indicating the cold weather outside, a sharp contrast with the pleasant warmth within. The basement club had a cosy and welcoming atmosphere, the smell of cigar smoke and Christmas pudding lingering in the air, and Edith felt immediately at ease. The guests were all scattered around, some on Alvar Aalto chairs, some standing next to the fireplace. The Isobar was a place famous for socialising, where you could meet some of the most compelling writers, artists and architects of the age, and everyone there had a drink in their hand and was engaged in heated conversation. She overheard a group lamenting that England was never to have a Bauhaus movement of its own.

Edith mingled among the guests, all Jack and Molly's friends. Edith's sharp eye recognised the writer Herbert Read, and Ernst Freud, the son of Sigmund, who had also emigrated to London and settled in a house in Hampstead. Edith grabbed an onion soup and found a corner to eat. Molly noticed and came over, bringing Wells Coates with her.

The night had cast a spell, the hours fleeing without pause and yet they remained, frozen in memory.

Allan Foote, nicknamed Jim in Geneva, and Len Beurton were Ursula's two new catches, both Englishmen who knew each other from the British Brigade in Spain. They had been proposed as potential assets after proving their courage in the past and were now due to work in Germany, in Munich and Frankfurt respectively.

When Ursula interviewed them, she did so without revealing any details about herself, not even her name. She analysed their behaviour, looks, body language and expressions, scribbling in her notebook as she did so. She had to be confident with her choice for the mission before she could reveal it to them.

Jim:

Early thirties.
Tall and a bit overweight.
Pale complexion with reddish hair.
Blue eyes.
Middle-class background.
Good appearance, all in all.
A fast thinker – grasps things quickly.
Asks sensible questions.
Good response in the face of new situations
and the capacity to adapt fast.
Resourceful.
Self-assured, has poise.

Len:

Twenty-five years old.
Thick brown hair.
Lean and athletic.
Hazel eyes and eyebrows that meet.
Strong appearance.
Looks half shy, but on the other hand also aggressive.

No interest in material things.
Extremely sensitive.
Well-read and intelligent.
A little clumsy with logistical matters.
His reputation in the brigade: absolutely fearless.
Father killed in the war.
Godfather was an admirer of Germany and
encouraged Len to travel around the country
and learn the language.

Both knew that it was a dangerous mission for which they were being interviewed. Once Ursula had confirmed their acceptance, she told them they were to be the GRU's eyes and ears, establishing themselves as acquaintances of the Nazis and collecting all kinds of information, especially concerning the Messerschmidt aircraft factory.

Both of the Englishmen were bachelors, and Ursula decided to start her divorce proceedings with Rudolf in order to organise a pro-forma marriage with one of them. Now settled in Switzerland, she had made her home in a farmhouse called La Taupinière, 'The Molehill', near Caux, a village in the French side of the country. Situated on top of a hill at a height of 1,200 metres and with a beautiful view of Montreux and Lake Geneva, it reminded Ursula of their home in Zakopane in Poland. She enjoyed being in nature and living in a village, and the location was truly idyllic, the beauty of the wild narcissus field behind the house attracting visitors.

The house itself was a typical Swiss farm house built entirely from wood, with the living quarters located at the front of the house and the stable at the back, home to a dozen cows. François, the farmer, lived just down the road.

There was also a hayloft, which would make a good hiding place for the transmitter – now functioning over a distance of 2,000 kilometres – and her other illegal material. Their new home was perfect.

Edith met Arnold for tea on the deck of the Isobar, with Tommy playing at her feet. He told her that Percy Glading, co-founder of the Communist Party of Great Britain, who Edith had lived with when she first married Alexander, had been arrested. Arnold wanted her to think of anything that might incriminate her, and to be aware of what might be coming. In his flat was a Leica camera that Edith had purchased for him. He had been using it to photograph documents stolen from Woolwich Arsenal.

That was the last time she saw her lover. She wished she'd taken in more details of how he'd looked, or the sound of his voice, or even what they ate. In the midst of Stalin's purges and show trials, he was recalled to Moscow and she never heard from him again. His death, like his life, was shrouded in secrecy. She liked to think he lived happily into old age, but she doubted it was true.

Not long after her last meeting with Arnold, and well before she knew it had been the last, Edith was getting ready to take Tommy out food shopping as she often did. Winter was beginning to thaw, and small buds or leaves were pushing out from the Hampstead trees. As she gathered her things for the market, two severe-looking men in Mackintosh coats appeared at her doorstep and rang the bell. Edith was taken aback and made sure Tommy was in his room and out of the way before opening the door. For but a moment she thought they were going to announce that something awful had happened to her husband, but they stepped into the hallway with intent and gave her their card, asking her to please follow them for questioning.

Edith acted surprised and told them that she would of course answer their questions but must first drop her son off at a friend's house around the corner. She confirmed that she would come back and meet them at the same spot.

The two men didn't look convinced and insisted on escorting her. They accompanied Edith to Lawn Road Flats, where Edith prayed that Molly or Beatrix would be home to look after Tommy. Beatrix was out, but Molly was there with her two boys. As soon as Molly saw Edith's face, she knew something was horribly wrong. Molly took Tommy in her arms and smiled at Edith, showing that she understood.

Edith returned to the men and stepped into their car showing no signs of distress, even though drops of cold sweat were running down her back. The shorter of the men started the engine and accelerated smoothly. Alone in the rear seat, Edith kept quiet and considered how she might answer their potential questions.

When the car approached Queen Anne's Gate and made a right turn, Edith immediately understood she was being taken to the Secret Police Headquarters, an imposing complex of buildings on the river. The car was checked and all her belongings taken away. She entered a block that appeared to be empty and was shown along a corridor to a lift and up to the first floor. She was searched again, this time more thoroughly and by a policewoman.

During all these procedures Edith kept her mind focused on preparing herself for the worse. Edith had no knowledge of what had happened after Percy's arrest. Only one thing was sure: she must be careful not to give away anything during the interrogation to come.

Edith sat and waited in the corridor. She wondered who would ever find out what had happened to her if they arrested her today? And what would become of Tommy?

The taller officer appeared again, now in uniform, and this time asked her to follow him. They entered a room where other men were already seated, one in front of a desk, another at the back and the smaller officer in an armchair, his face unnervingly impassive. The sharp, acrid smell of disinfectant and the glare of the strip lights made her nauseous as she was kept waiting for what felt like an eternity. Eventually a young officer walked in and proceeded to question her with a simmering aggression, his blue eyes searching as she turned her gaze to the file, her file, laid out on the desk between them:

– *Yes, it is me … it is actually Tudor-Hart.*
– *I don't understand … this is an invoice?*
– *Percy Glading? Sorry, no idea who that is.*
– *But that is not my address. I live on Alexandra Road and my name is Tudor-Hart.*
– *I am a photographer by profession.*
– *No, a press photographer.*
– *I buy and sell a lot of cameras.*
– *No, I can't recall this specific Leica.*
– *If another person has been taking pictures with a camera of his own and freely bought, what implicates me in these acts, may I ask?*
– *It is not my camera.*
– *Right now I am worried about my son. Can I go to him as soon as possible? He is only two years old.*
– *I swear that the camera you found is absolutely not mine.*
– *I myself can't imagine how this invoice has appeared.*
– *It must be, without a shadow of a doubt, a mistake.*
– *Of course I am ready to write and sign the declaration.*
– *Thank you.*
– *I will find my own way out, thank you.*

As she traversed the interminable corridor, she kept her composure. She had not given any information, just as Arnold had instructed her.

She walked out of the headquarters towards the taxi rank and collapsed into the back seat of a cab. She felt herself decompressing as she asked the driver to take her to Lawn Road Flats, and she longed to be reunited with Tommy. It had been a stark reminder of all she was risking through her involvement in the Communist Party. And Tommy needed her.

Edith ran up the Isokon building stairs, two at a time, to Molly's flat. As Molly opened the door, Tommy leapt towards her, flinging himself into Edith's open arms. In that moment Edith knew what was truly important in her life. She needed to protect him at all costs.

Edith thanked Molly for her generosity and kindness towards them. She had given Tommy a light lunch and reassured him that his mum would return soon. In the meantime he'd been preoccupied by the many toys she brought out for him.

'Don't hesitate Edith,' Molly said. 'I am always here for you and Tommy if you need me in the future.' Her words were infinitely soothing. Edith had been feeling so lonely. Then Molly stopped, a little awkwardly. 'He is a gorgeous child, really so sweet and dear. He doesn't speak or interact much though,' Molly said carefully, and Edith felt her blood cool in a way that was almost worse than the interrogation. 'If you ever want to take him to a professional, I can personally recommend Anna Freud.'

'He's still only so little,' Edith said. 'But thank you.'

'Of course,' Molly said, 'it's nothing to worry about.'

That evening at home, when it was still and Tommy was fast asleep, Edith burned her negatives.

URSULA

Jim and Len had become close friends now that their mission had united them, but geographically they were apart, Len in Frankfurt and Jim in Munich. Len was boarding with a widow and her son, whose interest in him developed into a series of cultural trips and some amateur German tuition. It was through his host that Len had the opportunity to visit the airport in Frankfurt where the Trans-Atlantic Zeppelin was on show. And it was during that excursion that the idea of sabotage occurred to him.

He returned to the airport many times, checking every detail to ensure his plan would have the best possible chance of succeeding. After much reconnaissance, he concluded that yes, they would be able to hide an incendiary device the size of a matchbox in the zeppelin's seat padding. Now all that was required was the assent of Jim, Ursula and the Centre, but this was not forthcoming on Jim's part. Jim threw doubt on the logistics of the explosion and worried about risking their necks with such a risky move right in the heart of Nazi Germany. But it wasn't long before an alternative presented itself.

One day as Len and Jim were walking in Odensplatz, renamed 'Square of the Martyrs', they encountered an SS parade in commemoration of the fallen Germans sent to support Franco in his civil war. Jim and Len quietly watched the parade go by and then turned off into a residential street.

There was an Italian trattoria on the right-hand side on the corner of Elisabethstrasse, and they decided to take refuge in this unassuming place. They were shown to a table next to a dark-haired young woman, where they sat without saying much as an eerie atmosphere pervaded the restaurant, abnormally quiet for such a busy time of day. Anticipatory tension was all around them – in the woman nervously fussing over her appearance, the staff conversing in hushed tones – and Jim and Len stared at one other perplexed.

Another young woman, tall and blond, joined the dark-haired one, sitting next to her without saying a word. But they were both clearly still waiting for something to happen and looked bored in each other's company.

Suddenly the silence was broken by the forceful opening of the double doors at the entrance, and two SS officers marched in and stood motionless in the middle of the trattoria.

Immediately afterwards, a man of stern features, with a tailored suit and a narrow, neatly groomed moustache arrived, and the owner came to greet him with a tremulous handshake and guide him and his crew to the next-door room. Jim and Len couldn't believe what they were witnessing until someone approached their table and asked them to put out their cigarettes – the Führer didn't like the smoke.

They stubbed them out and ordered food, but all they could think about was getting out of the restaurant to speak openly of what they had experienced. Clearly the dark-haired girl was Eva Braun. All kinds of ideas were racing through their minds as they ate mechanically.

This restaurant might be a golden opportunity, they later told Ursula and the Centre. They were so close to Hitler that he could smell their cigarettes.

But before a decision could be made, events overtook them.

EDITH

In August 1939, Edith and Alexander were listening to the radio in her living room. Alexander had returned to his family, but he was not the man she had once loved. Their bond was irrevocably broken, and the only subject of common interest was their son – yet Edith did not think that Alexander's presence was good for Tommy anymore. He seemed absent, drained and exhausted. Moreover, he seemed even more impatient and nervous than he did before he left. Everything Edith did seemed to irritate her husband, and Tommy was in the middle of it all, observing everything.

It was then that the greatest shock of their lives happened: when the news programme came on the wireless, the announcer declared that Stalin and Hitler had signed a pact of non-aggression. This was almost inconceivable. Edith and so many of their friends had given everything to the fight against Fascism. How could Stalin have made a deal with Hitler?

As Tommy slept in his bedroom, they stayed up talking, making excuses, trying to find reason behind the madness. Perhaps it was a ruse to trap the Germans, they wondered? But really, they knew this was a devil's alliance. It squandered all their efforts, their sacrifices and beliefs. Two bitter ideological enemies had joined forces in an act of pure treason that could never be undone.

Edith had many German Communist friends who had fled National Socialism and sought refuge in the Soviet Union. Now Stalin handed them back to the Germans, and they were sent to concentration camps. It didn't take long to find out about the secret agenda behind this pact – there was a hidden clause, an agreement between Germany and the Soviet Union to divide up and portion out the countries that lay between them. Germany would take Western Poland and part of Lithuania. The Soviet Union would have Eastern Poland, the Baltic States and part of Finland. Just a week after Alexander and Edith listened to the radio announcement, Germany invaded West Poland. Two weeks after this, the Soviet Union attacked the East.

Since Britain and France had guaranteed to protect Poland's borders, on 3 September 1939, war was declared. While the external world fell apart, so did Edith's domestic landscape. Alexander was unable to deal with the unbearable failure of his ideology and became severely depressed. One night, out of the blue, he decided to leave everything behind. This time he didn't even warn Edith.

Children were being evacuated from cities all over Britain and sent to the country with the help of volunteers. In the first few days of the war, one and a half million evacuees were sent to rural locations from London alone, but they soon began to trickle back into the cities, lulled into a sense of security by a lack of direct action from their enemy. This, however, was a trick, and on 7 September 1940, the Blitz began. In just a few hours, 430 people were killed and around 1,600 were badly injured.

In Germany, after the devastating pact of non-aggression with the Soviet Union, the Centre had put the sabotage plan on hold. In fact, it had become very dangerous for Len and Jim to stay in the country at all. Ursula was informed that she had to get them both back to Switzerland. They left their hosts on the pretext of a long family holiday back in England.

Everything happened so quickly: the Swiss army mobilised, Danzig was occupied by Hitler's troops, Poland was invaded and war declared.

Len and Jim managed to get out of Germany and into Montreux, where Ursula had booked them rooms in a hotel. It also happened that Ernst was passing by Switzerland to visit his mother, and he delayed the continuation of his trip at the last moment to visit Ursula and see his daughter for the first time. Janina was already three years old. Ursula had mixed feelings about Ernst's visit – he never had a relationship with his daughter anyway and she thought this could only complicate matters – but she was nevertheless thrilled to see him again. And when it was time to say goodbye, her looming separation from both Ernst and Rudolf was more daunting than ever – one could smell war in the air, and it seemed only a matter of time before the Swiss were caught up in it.

Ursula was sitting on the terrace of a café in Lausanne, dressed casually while waiting for someone to join her at the table. It was a beautiful sunny day and she enjoyed observing pedestrians as they passed.

A man approached her and without a word sat her table. She had been waiting to hear from the Swiss Federal Intelligence Service, but who would appear and why, she knew not. There was no introduction – he went straight to the point: 'We have received information suggesting that you have installed a radio transmitter,' he said.

Ursula didn't look surprised, hiding her nervousness well. She had nothing to fear really, since the transmitter was perfectly hidden. No one would ever be able to find it. She answered confidently:

'Absolutely not. May I ask, where did you get this idea from?'

'The girl who delivers your groceries wouldn't invent a story like that if she hadn't seen it.'

'You can come to my house and look if you think it necessary,' Ursula said, 'but to save you the trouble, may I ask what exactly she thinks she saw?'

'She saw a Morse key in your house.'

Then Ursula started to laugh and replied: 'That's a toy belonging to my nine-year-old. We could go together to the toyshop and find it there? That's where I got it from.'

'No need for that at this point,' the officer answered, somewhat irritably.

But the questioning went further, with Ursula prompted to tell the story of her family. They had had to emigrate from Germany and flee the Nazis. She said that her father was a professor, and that he'd given her a small amount of capital, from which she received enough income to live on.

The truth was that she received money from the Centre, which she put in her account in England as a reserve for her children. But since the war started, she had found herself in financial difficulties.

As he was about to leave, Ursula couldn't stop herself from saying one last thing:

'You know, I am offended that a neutral and democratic country like Switzerland expresses distrust towards us Germans persecuted by the Fascists. Why not instead focus on all the Nazis infiltrating the country?'

Ursula extended her information-gathering network to include well-informed journalists, who enjoyed swapping notes and her engaging conversation. Being based near Geneva and having access to information from the

League of Nations was also quite useful. There were all sorts of agents and double agents hovering around the city at this time.

Len and Jim visited Ursula daily at her home, where she taught them spycraft and they experimented with sending messages using the Morse key. She passed on everything she had learnt at school about the construction and functioning of the radio transmitter.

Ursula enjoyed the company of Jim and Len. Although they were very different from each other, for a long time the three of them complemented and supported each other.

Len loved nature and accompanying Ursula on her walks and hikes. Equally, he enjoyed spending time with her children and took an interest in their education. He was drawn to Ursula's identity as a mother as much as a spy. Jim, being the more lethargic of the two, often stayed behind when Len and Ursula went on their excursions, and so Ursula and Len spent a lot of time alone together.

They got closer and closer, and the introvert Len opened up to her, telling stories about his childhood and his fears. He told her his father was killed in the First World War before he could meet his son, and his mother sadly couldn't take care of him. She found another family willing to take him in exchange for a small weekly sum. She promised to visit regularly and take him on holidays, but these things never happened.

Aged fourteen, Len became a lorry driver in a quarry. His obsession with vehicles and engines took him further and he was soon a car mechanic, and by now he could repair and operate any machine he encountered – the handiest man around.

Ursula was beginning to see Len as more than just a comrade, yet she was supposed to be entering into a marriage of convenience with Jim. He was a good asset – his natural talent for making friends was invaluable. So Ursula tried to ignore her feelings for Len.

Life was frugal for Ursula since she had to support her children and her housekeeper and former nanny, Ollo, as well as Len and Jim. She also had expensive legal bills, as despite Rudolf's letter in aid of the process, the solicitors' visits kept coming. Her ever-increasing responsibilities were starting to gnaw away at her. And then there was the worry of whether they could be safe where they were. The Swiss were neutral on the face of it. However, they had accommodated the blackout requests from Nazi Germany. And they not only continued to produce weapons for the Germans, but also facilitated the flow of war materials from Germany through Switzerland into Fascist Italy. Living in Switzerland, Ursula felt that most of the Swiss population was against the Fascists and hated Hitler. But with the government facilitating the enemy, the question of who could be trusted was always on her mind.

And this question was becoming ever more important as rumours swirled about potential Swiss anti-immigrant legislation. There was already a decree that prohibited Jewish refugees from being granted the ability to work. Attaining an English passport had become a vital concern. She was separating from two men and in need of another – this time a Brit. People would disappear sometimes, and it was almost impossible to find information about their whereabouts. A comrade of Ursula's stopped turning up to their meetings and she found herself unable to trace him. She visited the place where he supposedly lived, but they confirmed he hadn't been there for weeks. She spoke to others who knew him, but nobody could tell her a thing. Frustrated at this roadblock, she asked a contact in Shanghai to trace her friend, without giving up any details of why she needed him found.

The friend was German, and it turned out that the Gestapo had demanded he be extradited back to Germany. Ursula was silent on the other end of the phone as this message was related to her. Her mouth was dry, and even the most basic response felt beyond her reach.

'Thank you for your assistance,' she managed to whisper.

One day Jim approached Ursula in the kitchen as she was preparing a snack for the recruits she was teaching. She stopped and turned to face him.

'Can we have a chat about the future?' Jim asked.

'Of course.'

'I know I originally agreed to marry you once your divorce papers were ready but—'

'Did something happen?'

'I have to admit that I promised a girl in England I would marry her. And therefore I just don't think it's a good idea for me to go ahead with our plan. It might cause some damage to our relationship.'

'I understand, but you accepted the plan. The Centre needs me to be protected.'

'Would you consider marrying Len instead?'

On the 23rd of February, the anniversary of the Red Army, Ursula and Len were married.

War was everywhere. Fascist armies were in Norway, Denmark, Netherlands, Belgium and Luxembourg. Micha's school had closed down, and Ursula decided to send him to a boarding school in Glion, a village overlooking Lake Geneva. It was a good move for his education although she was sad to be separated from him.

A perilous phase had begun and uncertainty was everywhere. It wasn't easy to live with the delicate and sensitive Len, and Ursula found him trying when quick decision-making was required, particularly when it came to parenting, but Ursula had a much greater danger facing her.

Ollo knew too much about Ursula. She was a part of the family, though, and would never betray them, or so Ursula assumed.

74

But when Ollo overheard Len and Ursula discussing a possible move to England, she felt abandoned. Ollo knew she could not be included in these plans because of her German passport and citizenship. The painful prospect of having to separate from the children soon drove her into a state of near insanity. She stopped talking and eating. She stopped sleeping. She was completely derailed at the thought of losing her family, particularly little Nina.

Ursula tried to talk gently with her and suggested she might like to have some time off work to relax. This idea backfired enormously: Ollo broke down and declared it unbearable to live here in these circumstances – after the betrayal, she could not stay in the house any longer and would be moving in next door with the farmer and his wife.

It sounded reckless and awkward to Ursula. Why would she want to live with the farmer? But it wasn't long before the motive became apparent. Her desperate plan was to stop the family from leaving Switzerland by betraying them in return and denouncing them to the authorities. The hope was that if something awful happened to Ursula, Ollo would automatically become the guardian of Nina and she could then take the little one to Germany.

As luck would have it, the authorities were unable to understand what Ollo was saying because she spoke such broken English. Her efforts to convince the farmer's wife that Ursula was involved in undercover activities also failed. Ursula admitted to hating Fascism in all its forms but maintained convincingly that any accusation beyond this was just the fantasy of a delusional woman.

Without Ollo in the house, Len had to take care of Nina whenever Ursula was at meetings in Geneva. And they had to keep a close eye on Ollo, who was always hovering around trying to get close to the child. Luckily the farmer's wife herself hated the Fascists and Hitler and told Ursula that she was unsettled by Ollo's behaviour. She wanted Ollo to leave her home.

With the situation deteriorating on all fronts both within and without the house, and with Ollo gazing over from the farmer's house through binoculars, Ursula sent Nina to a German boarding school called Les Rayons, founded by the famous educator and director Kurt Hahn.

They were slowly coming round to the realisation that leaving Caux was the right decision, but they would have to do it carefully without awakening any suspicion. Ursula was fond of La Taupinière and enjoyed the lake, the mountains and the beautiful landscape. She was also a keen skier, so it was difficult to detach herself from her life there. Every day she found such deep joy in the place, and it was painful to tear herself away.

But then a message came from the Centre.

We suggest that you and Len move to England now.

So there it was.

The journey began in Geneva on 18 December 1940 at seven in the morning. Ursula had taken the kids out of boarding school, and they all stepped on to the unheated bus, embarking on the long trip to England. In order to reach Spain and then Portugal, though, en route to England, they had to cross Vichy, a small corridor in France governed by the Nazis' puppet government. Despite much anxiety, their passage through enemy territory was uninhibited.

But having made the long bus ride to Portugal, there was one problem: Len had been unable to get a transit visa in Spain and so had to stay behind. Franco was keen to show his friendship to Hitler and was blocking the passage of British citizens eligible for military service.

After a three-week-long voyage on board a steamer, Ursula and the children finally arrived in Liverpool.

But the entry to England was controlled, and Ursula stopped – the only person taken aside for interrogation:

'Are you travelling alone?'

'Where is your husband?'

'What is the reason he is not accompanying you?'

'What are your plans?'

'Where are you heading to, and where will you stay while in England?'

'What is your source of income?'

Everything seemed gloomy, cold, damp and unfriendly. But Ursula kept calm and answered all the questions as best she could. She wanted to find a hotel for the night and to put the children to sleep. They were exhausted and sick from the strenuous trip.

She managed find them a hotel next to the harbour, but not even an hour had passed before the sirens howled. Ursula woke the children up and dragged them to the cellar where they would all be sheltered from the air raid.

So the new challenge was to find a place that would be safe from the endless bombardment for the rest of their stay. Ursula's parents were living with some friends in Oxford, escaping the heavy bombing in London, which she, too, sought to avoid. But soon they would have to move back to London because their friends in Oxford needed the rooms for their own relatives. Oxford was safe and suffered very few air attacks, so it was difficult to find a place of their own there.

Morale was still strong among the population, even though the English had been enduring defeat after defeat since the beginning of the war. By now the hope that Hitler would fight the Soviet Union instead of the Western powers had long dissipated. The reality was something else. The Conservatives and Chamberlain had miscalculated, but once they realised it, they were prepared to face it. And then Churchill had motivated the whole country to resist the Fascists, asking for 'blood, toil, tears and sweat' from his people.

As the days went by, Ursula started to question ever more why the Centre hadn't contacted her since she'd arrived in England. Their appointments had been pre-arranged from Switzerland, but at the agreed times no one would appear.

And she was still struggling to find a place to rent. Three members of her family and their spouses, as well as her uncle, were all living in Lawn Road Flats. But Ursula didn't want to impose herself on her brother or sister. They were all living on minimum income and in small apartments. And anyway, she knew she was under observation and didn't want to subject her family to the same scrutiny.

The countryside would be ideal, but many places there didn't want to take in foreigners, and if they didn't mind then the prices were steep. Finally Ursula found a bungalow some three miles outside Oxford. It seemed perfect, except that it was expensive and she had to use her savings to pay the rent.

Her worries increased daily. She was unable to help Len get to England with his papers. And adding to her troubles was the news of Rudolf's arrest in China. Apparently he'd been arrested while building a transmitter and was only released through the efforts of the Centre.

But Ursula was still eager to continue her work and have an impact. And when she went to London for one of her prearranged meetings, at last there was a turning point in her fortunes.

Ursula was at the meeting place scanning her surroundings for anyone who looked like an agent. She was wearing a light dress, and it was a typical May afternoon, sunny and mild. All the flowers were in bloom, but the atmosphere of war made everything feel sombre and dispiriting.

A man approached and greeted her with the code words. She took the lead and walked a few streets further so they could find a place to talk.

The Soviet agent Sergei congratulated Ursula on her arrival in England and handed her some money. Ursula was so relieved. He explained that he had had an accident and that was the reason why he couldn't meet her at their previous appointments. Sergei was clear in this message: the Centre needed news. He relayed a list of her new duties.

'We want you to acquire new contacts ... with political figures and with the military,' he said.

Ursula listened carefully, already scheming ways to acquire find these connections.

'It is very important to build an information network,' he continued, increasingly confident he was speaking with the right person. 'When will be the transmitter set be running?' he asked.

'Very soon,' she answered.

The beautiful spring sunshine continued unabated, and to cheer herself up, Ursula took a beautiful polka dot dress out of her wardrobe. Len hadn't seen it on her yet, and so she began a letter describing it to him, an image to hold on to while they were apart. She told him how sad she was that he was not coming to England. There were hundreds of things she wanted them to do together. She felt lonely without him.

Although originally they had both received the order to come to England, once he had been refused entry a comrade had convinced Len it was more important to stay in touch with Switzerland. And Len's file and request to emigrate had apparently been put on hold because there were more urgent cases that needed attention.

Ursula was not one to give up without a fight though. She remembered meeting Eleanor Rathbone, a Left-wing MP who had fought tirelessly for the lives of refugees, before the war and decided to write her a letter. She explained the absurdity of her soldier husband – a brave man who had fought for his country and against Fascist rule – being abandoned abroad.

The Labour MP made the government aware that a soldier needed the permission of His Majesty's Government in order to return to his home country, and not long after, the General Consulate in Geneva was contacted and told to issue a passport for Len. Soon he was on his way back to his wife.

Lawn Road, made of reinforced concrete around a steel frame, was a relatively safe place to live during the Blitz. A few blocks down the road, though, a dozen houses had been completely destroyed during an uninterrupted six hours of terror. During these raids, many of the Lawn Road tenants moved to the Isobar at night, since it was well equipped with emergency provisions. They sat under the giant poster of Hampstead, or on their plywood Isokon chairs, or slept curled up under the moulded plywood tables where they had lunched not so long ago. Though the BBC had shut its radio stations, the residents were kept informed about developments by the writers and journalists residing at the flats. They even produced a weekly bulletin called 'Comparative Broadcasts' for their neighbours.

Jack Pritchard found himself massively in debt due to the lack of income from his furniture business, as well as the finance and maintenance of Lawn Road. He took a job at the Ministry of Information, the government department responsible for publicity and propaganda. Meanwhile Wells Coates joined the RAF and began work on the development of fighter aircrafts. The kitchen chef of the Isobar restaurant also joined the RAF. Fortunately the new chef who replaced Harben at the Isobar was also quite resourceful and had managed to come up with some themed dinners despite the scarcity of ingredients during the Blitz.

Molly and Beatrix were both planning to move to Canada with their children, and Jack Pritchard suggested that Edith do the same, but Edith had neither the funds nor the contacts to achieve this. Moreover, she could not abandon her life's purpose, the fight against Fascism. Instead, she kept her child close and tried to find a job to earn some money for herself and Tommy, but there was nowhere to turn.

Tommy, like many children, was terrified of the bombs. He was three when the war started. Perhaps his psychological problems would have begun around this time anyway, with or without the horrific noise and the devastation of the London bombardments, there is no way of knowing.

Before the bombardment started Tommy had been a quiet, solitary child. He struggled to sleep, and his facial expressions often did not match his feelings. He did not enjoy make-believe games, unlike other children his age, and was self-contained. But when the sirens started and the stillness descended, planes appearing overhead, Tommy would scream so hard he'd throw up. His cries wouldn't stop. He lashed out and fought Edith. His body shook at night. The few words he said came out with a stutter, and he clung to her constantly, day and night.

After the Blitz began, for fifty-seven nights there was no day without at least one alert and usually there were multiple. Tommy's anxiety skyrocketed. He rocked back and forth, hit his head against walls compulsively and was constantly agitated. Any disturbance of his routine was met with panic and anger. Edith was torn. Evacuating him to the countryside would be safer, but how might he decline without Edith there to look after him? Could someone else, or an institution, be trusted with him when he was in this state?

Edith knew, too, that she was being watched. She had not been forgotten by MI5 after Percy Glading's arrest, and this threat hovered like a cloud over her head. But she was careful to avoid a trail of evidence, never even getting paid by the Soviet secret service for her work. All that MI5 saw was a mother trying to help her severely traumatised son while making enough money to get by. MI5 watched her as she found a steady job at an Edgware Road photography studio focusing on art and fashion. They watched as she consistently brought Tommy to meet the pioneering Austrian-Jewish child psychoanalyst Anna Freud, hoping that Tommy could find some relief from his suffering.

In 1941, Germany invaded the Soviet Union. It was the largest land offensive in human history, with over ten million combatants taking part. Intelligence sent to Stalin by Kim Philby, along with another Soviet Spy named Sorge, instigated the gradual but increasingly certain defeat of Hitler's armies. While seventy-eight German divisions were primed on the outskirts of Moscow, Philby confirmed another source's intelligence that the Japanese were planning to strike in the south and so were no longer a threat to the Soviet Eastern Front. Stalin now pointed a million men, as well as new guns and tanks, towards Hitler's troops, and the German losses were extraordinary.

If Edith had not introduced her former lover to Kim, who knows how the world would look like now.

Edith was living a quieter life than ever, or at least trying to. She too had moved out of London to avoid the bombing and give Tommy a little peace. She enjoyed walking by Gravesend where the Thames reached the sea. Sometimes she walked with Tommy, and sometimes with her old family friend from Vienna, Engelbert Broda. She looked forward to meeting Berti, as he was known, and spending the day on the estuary while Tommy was looked after by a neighbour he trusted. There was always a breeze there, and it was one of the few places where Edith felt she could breathe deeply.

Berti was an Austrian physical chemist. He had left Austria in 1938 after being imprisoned multiple times for his involvement with the Communist Party. He now worked in Britain's Cavendish nuclear laboratory in Cambridge but often came to London and from there would make his way out to see Edith. She felt grateful to be in the company of someone from her old life, who had been to her family bookshop and known the same people. She still missed Litzi desperately, and her life had been so hard since Alexander left. But walking with Berti on sunny autumn days, their movements soothing and the light soft, Edith felt as if she could finally unburden herself of the pain she had carried in London. All the other people walking by the river were in their own worlds. Nobody was watching her.

Edith told Berti things she had never discussed with anyone. About Tommy and Alexander, divorce and therapy. About bombs and sadness. Soon they found their hands touching lightly as they walked. Later, they became lovers.

Edith was perhaps incapable of apolitical love, and nothing was simple with her desires. First complication: Berti was married. Second: Berti became the assistant to astrophysicist Hans von Alben, who was experimenting with nuclear chain reactions. So Berti had access to large amounts of information about the Manhattan Project, the research programme tasked with producing the first nuclear weapons. Through Edith, Berti passed atomic secrets to the Soviet Union. Third, and knottiest, complication: Tommy, now six years old, hated Berti.

Ursula, meanwhile, was working as a courier for the USSR's 'Atomic spies': Klaus Fuchs and Melita Norwood.

The women did not know it, but they were conspiring together, these dedicated mothers and Communists who had collided at the Isokon launch and passed one another uncomprehending who knows how often, were both hastening the development of the Soviet atomic bomb, successfully tested in 1949.

Tommy's behaviour had deteriorated to the point where Anna Freud was at a loss and suggested a new direction in the form of Dr Donald W. Winnicott. While Edith nervously prepared to visit him, searching for clothes and making breakfast, an envelope dropped through the letterbox. It was from Alexander, and Edith felt joyful because it meant he had been thinking of them. But her joy quickly faded when she read his words. He had been sending her fifteen pounds a month, but now due to some unexplained personal difficulties he was only going to be able to send her thirteen. Edith would need to make up the difference in order to pay for Tommy's therapy.

Edith smiled at Tommy and pretended everything was fine. Dressed, fed, they headed out on to the street.

Edith composed herself. She would be positive. No amount of money would be too much if the doctor could help Tommy. He had worked throughout the war with traumatised children and was well-respected.

As they stepped into the room, the doctor lifted his head and greeted them kindly. He was tall and elegant, his manner welcoming. The three of them sat at a round table in the corner of the room, a beautiful morning light softening the office interior, and the meeting began in an informal tone.

Dr Winnicott was positive. He believed that in less than two years of regular visits and treatment, Tommy would be able to join a normal school and show his real personality. The key, the doctor said, was that Edith must spend as much time as possible with Tommy and never leave his side. He must not be left with Edith's neighbour any more.

'But I have to go to work and earn money,' Edith said desperately. 'Otherwise how will we live?'

The doctor did not answer this question.

Edith's relationship with Berti took a grave turn one day when she went to hang his jacket in the wardrobe and found a piece of paper in his pocket with a short message scrawled on it: *Let me know when you arrive. Can't wait. Ina.*

She stood in front of the window, and as the morning light filtered through the glass and into the bedroom the shock subsided and she felt a deep sadness awaken inside her. She had never heard him mention Ina. Her mind filled with questions. She wanted to know more but was afraid of where they might lead.

Edith prepared dinner and set the table for three. That evening they all ate together, and then Edith took Tommy to bed and read him a story. Meanwhile Berti went to his desk and did a little work. When Tommy was asleep, Edith joined Berti in the living room. She approached him calmly and said with a tender voice, 'Who is Ina?'

Berti hesitated, but he knew that the time for hiding was over.

She was a poet and translator from Zagreb in Croatia. She and Berti had met and fallen in love before the war, he said, but were both married already. They'd kept in touch after Berti moved to London, but during the conflict she stopped replying to his letters and he thought something awful must have happened. Indeed, awful things had happened. Her husband and child were killed in front of her, but she had now miraculously emerged alive and had been staying in Rome. Berti was attempting to get a visa and would be travelling to find her.

'When were you going to tell me?' Edith asked, but it no longer mattered. The shattered pieces of her trust no longer fitted together.

Berti left that night. Edith sat at the table in her flat, and ideas and memories hovered, merging and diverging within the little room. The table in front of her was covered with images. These were photographs of others, and yet she saw similarities to herself in the vulnerable gaze of the workers and children. The social aspects of her work were intrinsically linked to her inner emotions and beliefs. Her subjects looked desperate, just like herself, longing for something to change.

So much had happened, personally and politically. Edith went over to her bookshelf and picked out a work by the Austrian Marxist Bruno Frei, whom she had first read sitting in the corner of her parents' bookshop. She wanted to curl up in her parents' bookshop again, full of idealism and indignation. Frei condemned the inequality of capitalism and expressed his vision of the dangers of rising antisemitism and nationalism. It was his words that first led her to the Social Democratic youth movement.

She linked her injustice to all the others visited upon the world and found solace. She would have this moment of introspection and then get herself together, knowing the battles yet to be fought and the bigger picture to be confronted.

Through her camera lens, Edith has always tried to tell the truth and draw attention to what people found uncomfortable to witness. Her hope was that by creating empathy she would rally people to her cause. Art is always and everywhere the secret confession, and at the same time the immortal movement of its time, as Karl Marx said.

She had started to feel the lines of her life blurring, a certain vagueness, a fraying around the edges of herself as if she were in two places at once – two rivers in parallel coursing across the same valley floor, plunging towards the same ocean. Maybe it began when Arnold went back to Moscow, or the first time she realised Tommy was seriously unwell. Sometimes she would dream of the opening of the Lawn Road Flats. Of the girl with the large nose and larger smile. She'd dream of Arnold, often, and where he might have ended up. She would wake up feeling as if she had not slept at all.

She would attend sessions alone with Dr Winnicott. He had coined the phrase 'the good-enough mother'. He connected the mothering process to the child's cognitive development and the development of a healthy concept of external reality. At first, the baby experiences the mother as part of themselves – it was a difficult, gradual process from complete dependence to a sense of separate identity. If this process was disrupted, as he believed had been the case with Tommy, then problems ensued.

She had developed a true admiration for Dr Winnicot, and each time she went with Tommy for a visit, her sense of trust increased. And then she dreamed that he had put his hand on her knee. Or was that real? In his office, hearing of her failings as a mother, eager to fix them and help her son, she had allowed his hands to comfort her.

His hand rose beneath her skirt, and it wasn't a dream or a nightmare but some warped reality. He was warm and kind and clever. He told her that he would leave his wife, that Tommy would get better, that they would all be together one day.

But Tommy was not getting any better. Tommy was having seizures, hitting her, attacking other children, and Edith was powerless to help her child. Tommy was only twelve. A child still, but she could see the man inside him and it terrified her. He was stronger than her already, and when he hit, which happened more regularly than she ever admitted to the doctor, there were significant bruises.

Edith would come up with excuses – she'd been clumsily walking into doors and table corners – as Winnicot undressed her in his sunlit office. But it became increasingly clear that neither Edith nor the doctor were helping their charge.

Alexander's father, who had once disinherited his son for being a Communist, agreed to pay for Tommy to go to a residential care facility on the doctor's suggestion. The doctor had proposed this without compassion in his voice.

Usually the office door would be closed, but that day it was ajar. Edith watched a little bird playing on the windowsill and then looked back towards the doctor's stern face. All his empathy seemed to have evaporated. She shivered, though the office was warm.

There was nothing more he could for either of them, he said. The only thing that could help Tommy was a structured environment staffed by expert carers who could help him develop confidence and independence.

It was the end. She approached to embrace the doctor, but he abruptly pushed her away and she fell stunned back on to her chair. It seemed an eternity before she stood up and walked away from him noiselessly, like a burglar.

Gradually loneliness invaded Edith's life. The war ended, and she was rarely in touch with Moscow. She visited Tommy as often as she could afford on her small salary as he was passed between hospitals, eventually ending up in The Royal Earlswood Institution for Mental Defectiveness in Surrey.

She barely slept, hardly ate. She started to question her own dedication to the Communist cause – but as always reassured herself that the fight against Fascism, however depleted its forces, and the struggle for working-class empowerment were still good reasons to continue. She was longing to hear from her old friends Litzi, Kim and Arnold. Through mutual acquaintances she heard that Litzi was living in East Berlin and had married a German journalist called Georg Honigmann. Clearly Litzi had broken her ties with the past for fear of jeopardising Kim.

Her one and only remaining friend was Anna Mahler, daughter of the composer Gustav and his wife Alma, who had also emigrated to London in 1939. Edith found solace in classical music, and they would meet once in a while and attend a concert together. It was therapy for her soul and reminded her of the time she would enjoy concerts in Vienna with Arnold.

Arnold was constantly in her thoughts and dreams. She liked to think of him lying back on his Long Chair, listening to his beloved Brahms, Haydn, Beethoven. The books everywhere, the window under the stairs that let in so little natural light but allowed secrets to stay hidden. What a price they had all paid.

After Len's return, Ursula's life began to pick up. The war reached its denouement with Len still waiting to be called up by the army, and Ursula travelled regularly to London for her work, recruiting agents.

Len had found Ursula settled and well-integrated into the community. But soon the harmony she had created came to an end. One day she was given notice by the owners of their place in Kidlington that it was time for them to look for something else because they needed it for their own family.

Ursula had a quick chat with Len and started to search for a new home. They ended up choosing a funny looking old house, with four bedrooms and a spiral staircase. It had a grassy patch in the backyard and an old shed that had originally been stables.

As soon as they moved in, Ursula's first mission was to install the transmitter. She knocked on the door of her wealthy neighbour. Ursula had heard that this neighbour adopted a Jewish child who had been in danger in Germany and gave them refuge in her house. She was curious to meet her.

Calling on her in the morning, she found Mrs Laski, wife of the famous Judge Neville Laski, lying in bed with layers of lace, having breakfast served on a silver plate. Ursula felt bad for intruding.

'I beg your pardon. I didn't mean to disturb you,' she said nervously.

'Not at all Mrs Beurton, do sit down and make yourself comfortable.'

Ursula sat next to her bed on a chair that the butler had placed for her, and instantly felt at ease. They discussed the war, the horrors of the Fascist machine, the terrors inflicted on the Jews, the inequality that plagued all Western societies, the hope that sprang from resistance.

She felt she could risk asking the question on her mind: 'Would you allow us to use one of your old stables to install an aerial antenna? It would run from our roof to the stable and be perfectly inconspicuous.'

'I don't see a problem with that.' She smiled mischievously.

'Thank you. I brought you a few homemade scones, if you'd like to try some.'

Time passed. And to outside observers their life appeared normal, uneventful as it largely was. Just a family of four and a perfect housewife with a proclivity for baking scones and offering them to the neighbours. Her Communist activities were few until one day Ursula got a message from her brother Jürgen saying that he had been contacted by a party member who needed to get in touch with the Centre. Jürgen gave Ursula the name of the interested comrade, Klaus Fuchs. The name rang a bell to her. She had the feeling that Jürgen had mentioned him before. She couldn't remember the exact context, although she seemed to recall he was based in Birmingham.

Ursula immediately went to the transmitter and sent a coded message to the Centre enquiring about him. Surprisingly enough, the response arrived quickly. Ursula was asked to establish a work relationship with Klaus Fuchs, but it had to be handled with extreme care and secrecy.

The meeting was arranged to take place a week later in a park far from the city. The location was ideal for Ursula - only a short distance from her house in Summertown, she could cycle there without difficulty.

On time and dressed inconspicuously, she parked her bicycle and then strolled along naturally, avoiding the impression she was looking for someone. And upon recognising her comrade, she immediately put her arm through his and they walked side by side. To an outsider they appeared lovers. Ursula felt better the moment they started to exchange a few words.

The conversation hovered around anodyne themes – books, films, nothing substantial – but Ursula noticed how intelligent and cultured this newly introduced comrade was. She enjoyed walking with him and found him very responsive. They didn't know anything about each other, but nonetheless a spontaneous connection was established without any effort on either side. If it were up to Ursula, they would have carried on for hours, such a fascinating personality was Klaus.

This was the beginning.

Ursula had navigated her first encounter successfully and soon received instructions for the second. She was intrigued by Klaus Fuchs and wanted to find out more about his activities. The information they passed between them seemed of urgent importance to the Centre.

The procedure was similar the second time they met. But this time the conversation was more to the point, and Klaus asked the questions he needed Ursula to transfer to the Centre. Through these questions, she could learn by inference more about the nature of his work.

She repeated these questions to herself while riding back home, and when she arrived the children were out and she took advantage of the free time to code the message carefully and transmit it to Moscow.

When the children returned, Ursula felt relieved and happy she had done all her work and so had time to spend with them. For the first time she could remember, her personal and professional lives seemed in good balance.

The encounters with Klaus were truly enriching, and he confessed just how much he appreciated their time together, their all-too-brief conversations that seemed to hint at so much more. Their closeness came with danger, and that brought them closer.

Everything went smoothly until one day he handed Ursula a thick book of almost a hundred pages. The look in Klaus's eyes told her that this chunky document was of huge importance. All she had to do was make sure it found its way to the Centre, but this was no easy task:

she would have to spend many hours working with great precision. And what made this task even more challenging was the urgency of the matter: 'They need this information as soon as possible,' he told her. Ursula knew she was in possession of top-secret documents, but their contents were unknown even to her.

Having failed to squeeze the document in her bag, she secured it in the basket with an elastic band and rode off, casting a final look behind to check she wasn't being tailed.

Klaus watched her leave. He never knew where she came from or went. They knew nothing about each other and kept it that way.

As she cycled home, she was already planning how to proceed. She had to drop everything and go to London as soon as she could to arrange the handover. But her priority for now was to hide the document safely for while she was gone.

She arrived at the edge of a nearby wood and, ensuring the coast was clear, began to pull away at the loose earth between the roots of an oak tree. This, her usual hiding place, would have to do. She placed the document there, filled the hole and then rushed home before the children returned.

Ursula caught the next train to London. Once seated aboard she sighed deeply. Not yet a sigh of relief – it was all still in front of her. She needed to find an agent who would take it to Moscow, but who could she trust?

Once at London Paddington, she hailed a taxi and directed it to a backstreet near the Victoria and Albert Museum. There she left a sign with chalk crumbs on the floor, indicating that she needed to contact the Centre urgently, specifically that evening.

On her way back home, she kept wondering about the document and the blueprints it appeared to contain. Would she ever find out its contents, or were they so secret that the Centre would keep them from her?

Strident knocks at the door woke Edith up in a panic. She feared the worst for Tommy. It took a minute for her to gather herself as she was still drowsy from the strong sleeping pill she had taken the previous night. As soon as she opened the door, a line of men walked in without permission and began to search her apartment.

They didn't miss a corner – every cupboard, shelf and piece of furniture was searched.

'You have no right to invade my private space,' she said.

'It is just a routine check,' one of them replied.

But of course, it wasn't. The men gave no further explanation, and she couldn't stop nor converse with them. So, she decided to call a lawyer friend who wasn't far away and ask him to come over.

It turned out that MI5, MI6 and members of the British Embassy were looking for traces of Kim Philby.

'Do you know where he's hiding?' one of them asked her.

Edith truly didn't. But the men didn't believe her and kept searching and searching in the vain hope of finding some clue about his whereabouts. In their frustration, they would occasionally stop for a moment and ask desperate-sounding questions:

'Is he hiding in East Berlin in the house of his ex-wife, Lizzy Honigmann?'

Edith's answers were as brief as possible: 'I don't know.'

She did her best to stay calm and wait for her friend, but even after his arrival, all they could do was stare as the men rampaged her apartment.

Unsuccessful in their pursuit, the men finally looked at each other and left, an enormous mess in their wake.

Two years after the first Soviet atomic bomb was tested, fearing that she was about to be unmasked, Ursula fled England back to East Berlin. Before leaving she stopped one last time to look at Lawn Road Flats.

On that day, too, Edith was in London dropping off some photographs in Hampstead, and she felt herself drawn to her former hunting ground. She arrived just ten minutes after Ursula had walked away, forever.

Leaves, glass, rubble and rubbish were strewn across the courtyard. The walls were stained and puckered and the windows blown out. This masterpiece of modernist architecture was no longer filled with optimism and intrigue.

She lifted her camera, hoping to turn this sadness into something of beauty. If she squinted, she could just imagine children playing on the balconies in blazing summer sunshine. She could imagine her friends Jack and Molly waving from their penthouse balcony, Alexander herding children up the stairs, Litzi and Kim sharing a joke.

She could imagine Arnold, smiling at her as she walked towards him.

URSULA

In 1950 Klaus Fuchs was unmasked and confessed to passing information on the atomic bomb to the Soviets. He disappeared off the face of the earth, presumed incarcerated.

Close to a decade later, Ursula was building a new career as a writer. In fact she had already published a bestseller about her life, *Ursula's Report*, in which she never mentioned the names of Klaus Fuchs, nor Melita Norwood.

She carried the memories of the past close to her but had stopped all activities with the Soviet Union. She recalled fondly one of her last missions. It was the time when her brother was working for the OSS, the forerunner of the CIA, and was approached by an American lieutenant whose mission it was to find German emigrants to return and spy on their fatherland. Ursula was asked to help and accepted without hesitation, as always.

Recruited from Communists, since they were the most dedicated in the fight against Fascism, the spies had to go through a full two-month training regimen before they were parachuted into different parts of the country. The fate of these brave men was continually on her conscience until, with an outpouring of rapturous joy, the war ended and the mission came to a stop, the spies freed from duty.

She enjoyed thinking back to the elation of 1945, the street party her neighbour Mrs Laski threw, the sense of community and mutual aid that flooded the country. Food was scarce but people gave each other what they had. A new world was possible. And the relief, the relief ...

One day as Ursula was walking in the park, always vigilant and wary of being followed, a habit she would never lose, she noticed a couple walking, deep in conference, a reminder of times gone by – elliptical conversations, half-meanings, half-truths. She followed them unthinkingly, to see them up close. Walking softly, incognito, images, impressions bubbling up: windswept walks along the estuary, transmissions sent in the dead of night, city skylines fading into the smog, switchback mountains and flooded paddy fields, leather-bound books with cracked spines, curls of smoke in the café lamplight, queues of the jobless in monochrome tableaux, a beer bottle smashed in celebration.

The man turned his head at an oblique angle, and she saw that it was Klaus Fuchs. She felt a cold shiver, relieved to see him alive. She wanted to approach him now that they were both safe in East Germany, so she followed the couple a bit further in her discreet way, perfected over the years. She didn't want them to notice her yet, but she had to make a decision – should she make contact, or was the past better left alone?

She resolved not to engage them but instead pass casually by. If he recognised her, she would stop and greet them.

By now her heart was pounding so strongly she thought they would hear its thrumming beat. She accelerated her pace and then slowed down a little as she got close, not wanting to seem in a rush.

She passed them gently on the side of Klaus. From her body invisible particles of heat rippled out into the crisp winter air.

She walked on, and on, and did not stop until she'd left them far behind. Ursula looked to the sky in search of an answer, but it was one that no one knew or would ever know.

NIGHT SHIFT

She sat in the dark of the attic,
Her hands following a flow
She was not able to read.
Words came confidently,
Or impatiently.
Occasionally stopping to
listen to the emptiness of the night,
Silence was her companion.
Sometimes an answer came,
but often it felt the words
were vanishing into the dark sky.
Her imagination ran:
Who would read her words and disconnected phrases?
She would never know.
Conversations with someone she couldn't see.
Everything impersonal,
including her personal life.
All part of a scheme, a large design.
A simple piece on a board game
Sometimes moved forwards,
Sometimes moved diagonally,
Sometimes from left to right,
And sometimes right to left.

RIGHT CENTRE LEFT
LEFT CENTRE RIGHT
CENTRE LEFT RIGHT
CENTRE RIGHT LEFT
RIGHT LEFT CENTRE
LEFT RIGHT CENTRE